# Exit the Bronx

Barry Singer

Exit the Bronx



Published in the United States of America in January 2022

ISBN: 978-0-578-31325-2

Cover Design by Ken Leeder

For my son Jed

# Contents

# Chapter One – Departure

**HSSSS...** The sound of the bus door opening and closing was like the sound of air escaping from an overfilled balloon. The great hissing noise continued until all thirty-five young men were aboard and ready to take the leap into the unknown. The New York Port Authority Bus Terminal was a spaceport, catapulting these young men to a new and uncertain life. Bob Sievers sat in row 12, happy to have a window seat. The big Greyhound slid out of the terminal, rushed through the Lincoln Tunnel, and traveled south past the oil refineries of New Jersey, en route to Fort Jackson, South Carolina, to deliver its cargo of fresh recruits. These thirty-five young men were about to begin a new and uncertain life in the U.S. Army, their cycle of basic training scheduled by the great military machine to begin the next day.

It was October 1966, and the Vietnam War was heating up. It was still early days in America's trip down the unhappy road that would end up somewhat resembling the Athenian disaster in Sicily almost 2,500 years before. During a long war with the Spartans, the Athenians opened a second front 1,000 miles away, in Syracuse. The huge distance, coupled with many tactical mistakes, cost the Athenians dearly. Learning from history is hard. No longer called "advisers," more than 500,000 U.S. troops were in Vietnam. The draft was taking about 35,000 men per month, and the lottery system had not yet begun.

Twenty-two-year-old Bob Sievers was one of those who had been drafted. He sat back to enjoy the trip, wondering about the future and reflecting on the past. He was getting a fresh start, for good or for bad, and no one needed a fresh start more than him. The world had been weighing on Bob since he was ten, and now, finally, change was palpable in every experience. Ironically, while his mother had come from Eastern Europe to find a better life in America, Bob would have to leave his country to do the same.

As the Greyhound raced down the New Jersey Turnpike, the man in the next seat introduced himself. "Hi, I'm Tom. Tom O'Reilly. Do you want half of a peanut butter sandwich?" He was tall and lanky, with short brown hair and a ready smile that showed a chipped front tooth. "My mom handed me a bagful of food as I left, and I can't eat it all."

"Thanks," Bob said. "But I filled up on bread and cheese, not knowing when I might eat next."

Actually, Bob had his own stash of food, along with a knife, fork, napkins, and salt and pepper. He liked to be prepared, a quality that would be helpful later.

"Where are you from?" Bob asked Tom.

"Pelham Parkway," said Tom.

The Pelham Parkway area in the Bronx was a place Bob knew well from all his trips to Orchard Beach in the summers. Living near the Grand Concourse, you were landlocked. It was a long trip to the beach. You got on the bus on the Grand Concourse going north. Then you changed buses at Fordham Road and traveled through the Pelham Parkway area to Pelham Bay Park, the home of Orchard Beach. Bob and Tom would become friends later, but right then, Bob wanted to just relax and think.

Bob had grown up in the South Bronx, on Morris Avenue and 170th Street, just opposite William Howard Taft High School, and just nine blocks from the Yankee Stadium. His family, while poor financially, was rich in friendships. The neighborhood was densely packed with neighbors and friends all around. Most of the apartment buildings were five stories tall, with two wings around a central courtyard. There were so many children that a three-year age difference was a vast, uncrossable gulf. If you were ten years old, all your friends were within a year of your age. You did not mess with thirteen-year-old kids, and they wanted nothing to do with you. To play on any day, you just stood in front of any nearby building and shouted "Who wants to play?"

There were many games to choose from. Stickball, off the point, and skully were a few of the popular ones. Stickball was played in the street with distances marked from manhole cover to manhole cover. The only equipment needed was a broom handle and a pink ball called a "Spaldeen," manufactured by the Spalding company. In this version of stickball, the batter stood in the middle of the street, between a pitcher and a catcher. Another popular version was played in the schoolyard without a catcher. In that version, a chalk-filled box representing home plate was drawn on a wall and the batter stood in front of it. For disputed pitches, you looked for the chalk on the ball. If there was chalk, the pitch was a strike.

School was always within walking distance. Buses and carpools were unheard of; they were a nicety of the affluent suburbs. Bob spent summers in a "bungalow colony" in Highland Mills, New York, about 40 miles north. Although poor financially, Bob's parents, Jake and Sarah, borrowed $1,000 from Citibank each year to pay for the Catskills summer. They paid the money back over the year, then started again the next summer.

Without a car, getting to the Catskills was difficult, but there was always a way. Bob's uncle ran a local fresh fish market and had a beautiful truck he used for the business. He would get up at 2 am each morning, drive to the Fulton Fish Market, and return with the fish for that day's sales. Uncle Warner's wife, Yolande, was Sarah's sister, and they lived with their two children in the same building. Warner was a generous spirit and always volunteered to transport the family to the bungalow colony at Highland Mills, New York.

They had great fun riding in the open back of the beautiful fish truck. It was a big truck with red-painted wooden slats on the sides. Riding in the truck and looking out through the slats was one of the best parts of the summer vacation, and Bob looked forward to it every year.

Jake and Sarah's apartment had two bedrooms. Bob shared one with his older brother, Henry. Despite the close quarters, Bob and Henry got along well. Outside the apartment, though, the three-year gulf in their ages separated them totally. They did play together when they were at home, though. They played Monopoly frequently, with Henry almost always winning. After about two hours, Henry would have most of the money and properties. One more landing by Bob on one of Henry's properties and it would be game over. At that point, Henry would offer to advance Bob some money in order to keep the game going as long as possible. Just like the wealthy do in real life. The game would continue for another half-hour or so until Bob, frustrated by being strung along, would bang the board up from the bottom, scattering the pieces and hotels around the room, thus signaling the end of the game. Because the game primarily depended on throws of the dice, Bob always told Henry he should consider a career in Las Vegas. But that was not to be.

Bob's life was good, and at age eight, the beginning of fourth grade and a new school beckoned. P.S. 53 was further than Bob had ever walked to school, about a mile or so, and in a different direction. Bob was thrilled to have this new adventure. After all, he was bigger now and could do more things independently.

The teachers were closely involved with the students and parent-teacher conferences were important, must-attend events. Teachers were in touch with the parents whenever needed and the students knew it, so they toed the line.

Bob enjoyed his time attending grades 4, 5, and 6 at P.S. 53. The most excitement occurred in the 6th grade, when Bob was "left back" (demoted one grade) for 24 hours. During a schoolyard softball game, Bob argued with a girl on the other team and finally, in frustration, told her she "was full of it." This tame rebuke sent the girl in tears to his teacher (who Bob said "shall live in shame forever"). The teacher "shot first and asked questions later," immediately demoting Bob back to the 5th grade. He called Bob's mother in for a face-to-face meeting at the school the next day. Bob's house was in turmoil that night, all because of what seemed like the most trivial of arguments. After one night back in the 5th grade, however, all was patched up when Sarah copped a plea with the teacher (who remains nameless). Bob was, of course, allowed to apologize and then be rightfully restored to the 6th grade, ending his 24 hours of banishment. Pretty exciting stuff for a ten-year-old.

Unfortunately, the year that began so well ended in disaster. Bob's father got very sick and began a downward spiral that ended with his death in 1960. His illness threw the whole family into chaos, and Bob's mother had to take a job in Manhattan four days a week to support them all. Although Bob could never have realized it at the time, his father's illness and the resulting turmoil would deal him a blow from which it would take sixteen years to recover.

Living near the Yankee Stadium had advantages. Baseball season kept Bob and his neighborhood friends busy collecting autographs. While most in the neighborhood were relatively poor, Bob and his friends were rich in friendships – and in baseball autographs, which became the teenagers' local currency.

Weekends were for hanging out in front of the stadium, waiting for the players to arrive. You approached the players, both visitors and Yankees, and asked for their autograph, handing the player a small, spiral-bound notepad and pen. Some days were good, others not so much. You learned who was a gentleman and who wasn't, and avoided the latter.

Yogi Berra, Phil Rizzutto, Elston Howard, Roger Maris, Hank Bauer, Billy Martin, Bill (Moose) Skowron, and Whitey Ford were among the many gentlemen you could count on to offer a smile and an autograph. A word or two also. "How are you today?" or "What are you studying in school?" It was a point of pride to be able to chat with such celebrities and heroes.

Others were not so nice. An unfriendly player once flung Bob's notepad and pen out onto the street.

"It was sad," Bob said. "He is a Yankee pitcher and should be a hero."

When a new kid came along, you warned them whom to avoid. Sort of like elephants teaching their young how to find the good waterholes.

Often, they went to the Concourse Plaza Hotel, the Yankees' home when they were in town. It was fun going through the revolving door and catching the players at just the right time. Knowing the techniques for autograph collecting provided a great sense of accomplishment, a source of pride, and a source of currency you could spend.

The biggest mystery was how Mickey Mantle got into the Yankee Stadium. In six years, Bob had not laid eyes on him once. The kids thought he had a secret tunnel, or perhaps arrived at the stadium by helicopter. That mystery was never solved.

Some visiting teams stayed at the Warwick Hotel in Manhattan at West 54$^{th}$ Street. The "collectors" would just hop on the IRT 4 Line at Jerome Avenue and 167$^{th}$ Street and be there in a half-hour.

What fun it was, walking through the lobby, going through the revolving door, and collecting autographs. They were on a mission. If by chance they saw James Dean or Elizabeth Taylor, who they'd been told stayed there, so much the better. Bob never saw either of those celebrities, but the autographs piled up. Several times, he met Early Wynn, a great pitcher for the Cleveland Indians who stayed at the Warwick. Wynn was a real gentleman, and friendly too. Bob always thought he must have a nice family.

The autographs were a currency used for a variety of games and events, from poker to sidewalk skully. Many years later, all Bob's autographs would be lost, but the idea of them, the memories of them, and their importance for the kids in the neighborhood could never be erased from his memory.

**Fort Jackson and Basic Training**

The big Greyhound eased off Route 95 at Florence, South Carolina. It traveled east on Interstate 20 for about one hour to Fort Jackson, South Carolina, now incorporated into the capital city of Colombia. Today, Fort Jackson is the largest basic training center in the U.S., training about 35,000 recruits per year.

The recruits exited the bus. Bob looked around and could hardly grasp the significance of his first sight of the place that would be his home for the next ten weeks. Far from the paved streets and parks of the Bronx, his world was now the opposite. The rural landscape was interspersed with a few buildings and training fields. And – ahh! – the smell and the feel of the Carolina red clay everywhere. Before long, though, Bob and the others got used to this complete change in sights, sounds, and smells. They even came to admire and like it.

They were assigned a barracks for the night, with the processing to begin the next day. Everyone grabbed a bed, unpacked lightly, and went to the mess hall for dinner. For the next ten weeks, the mess hall and barracks would be the center of the recruits' universe.

The next day was a blur. Awakened at 5 am, the recruits, now "trainees," began reception processing. They were issued uniforms, got buzz cuts (one size fits all), received basic physical examinations, and were assigned permanent barracks. By 5 pm, most had collapsed on their bunks, exhausted from the relentless schedule of events. Some of the trainees were in poor physical shape. Remember, this was the draft, not a volunteer group. Bob, though, was in great physical shape. From the age of fourteen, he had exercised regularly, lifted weights, and even studied judo and karate for two years. He was prepared physically. The big worry for most was whether they would go to Vietnam and what would happen there. Bob, also tired from the long day, rested in his bunk and slept.

Blam! At 5 am, Drill Sergeant Richard Murphy, Jr. entered the barracks. He turned on the lights and side-winded his stick across the metal of the bunks, creating a loud clanging alarm.

"Time to rise and shine, ladies. You have one hour to fall out on the street with beds made, shaved, dressed in fatigues, and in formation."

Drill sergeants were the front-line trainers. They had to learn what made each trainee tick. They pushed, prodded, and shouted at the trainees constantly. The process of turning a bunch of raw recruits with vastly different backgrounds and no knowledge of the military into a cohesive team, a fighting machine, had begun. At the same time, they were assessing how you reacted, seeing how much abuse you could take and still keep your composure.

The fighting group they were creating needed to obey orders instantly, treat one another as family, and trust one another, knowing they lived or died as a group. Many individual offenses resulted in group punishments to make that point. Those group punishments resulted in a variety of soul-searching, fistfights, and group meetings to iron out differences one way or another.

Most drill sergeants were African American or Latino. Richard Murphy Jr. was an African American who'd lived in the U.S. South his whole life, a career army soldier and combat veteran who had served two tours in Vietnam. Such men were serious soldiers, and you took them seriously if you were smart. Of course, not everyone in the incoming group was smart. The drill sergeant major who was responsible for the whole battalion was Jaimee Dominguez from San Juan, Puerto Rico, a decorated veteran and proud of his two years of civilian education.

After falling out on the street and learning how to be "in formation," the battalion went on a forced march of about five or six miles just to begin the day. Following the march, the group was allowed to go to the mess hall for breakfast. Bob loved the meals at Fort Jackson. Because he was slim to start with and burning thousands of calories each day, he could eat as much as he wanted. From the breakfast buffet, Bob chose three pancakes, two sunny side eggs on top, and a generous helping of table syrup on top of the whole stack. This became Bob's go-to breakfast for the next ten weeks. By noon, he had burned all those calories and was looking for more.

The rest of that first day was a series of classes and more physical training. They learned how to make a bed, something few of them had done before. The beds had to be made with precise "hospital corners" and the top cover had to be drum-tight so you could bounce a coin on it.

The drill sergeants, who entered the barracks at 5 am, tore apart the poorly made beds until about the 5th week when, at last, everyone had gotten it right. Part of the process!

Bob went to bed as early as he could that night and reflected on his situation.

He was handling the physical training easily and knew a good amount about the military already. At the City College of New York, Bob had joined the ROTC. This program consisted of two years of military training, after which you chose to stop or elect two more years of advanced training, a key decision point. Upon continuing, you were "committed" to the U.S. Army and would become a 2nd lieutenant upon graduation. Bob enjoyed the training and learning military history, command and tactics, map reading, orienteering, and many other subjects. His problem was that it was 1964, and Vietnam was heating up. The Johnson Administration was focused on the Great Society and left the Vietnam War to the Defense Department, which ultimately became obsessed with "ratcheting up the pressure" on North Vietnam in the false belief that a precise amount of incremental pressure would force Ho Chi Minh to the bargaining table.

U.S. troops in Vietnam were no longer advisers but combatants, and their number was growing dramatically. Now, exaggeration is one way to make a point, but Bob had read some stories that indicated the life expectancy of a 2nd lieutenant in Vietnam was about eleven seconds. Confusion, doubt, uncertainty, lack of coherent goals, and the distrust of officers on the part of the enlisted men in Vietnam were legendary.

So, in 1964, Bob declined the second two years of ROTC and took being an officer off the table but was willing to go into the U.S. Army if called.

The good news was that because of his two years of ROTC training, he was one of the few trainees in the battalion who knew something of the military. He was also in excellent physical shape, a combination that would be helpful in the weeks ahead. He had not always been so fit, he reflected, thinking back to when he was fifteen years old.

**Peter the Bully**

Bob's father had been ill for five years. With his mother working and his father needing attention, there were many blank spots in Bob's life experiences. Daily life consisted of Sarah's work as a sales associate at the Ohrbach's Department Store on 34th Street in Manhattan, the two brothers getting to school and back each day, and the care needed by Jake. Henry, Bob's older brother, was a senior in high school at the time, while Bob was only two years behind despite being three years younger.

Bob was excellent at his studies and got good grades, which resulted in him being taken into an educational experiment called the SPs. In this unfortunate program, a student was made to skip the eighth grade in what, for many, was an unwise acceleration of their education. Of course, Sarah and Jake were too preoccupied to carefully consider the foolishness of this program, so it happened. To make matters worse, Bob had already accelerated one grade because of his late-in-the-year birthday. So not only was Bob essentially two years younger than many of his high school cohorts, but he also started college in 1960 at age sixteen, two years younger than almost any other freshman at the City College of New York.

As he had a medium to slender physique and had grown up in a densely populated neighborhood, Bob had to make good choices of friends and enemies. Before he learned about the benefits of exercise, he was a typical 100-pound weakling. While not a problem among his friends, he was the perfect foil for any local bully. And as nature abhors a vacuum, sure enough, a bully appeared.

His name was Peter Herzog. He lived in the same area as Bob and was the same age and in the same grade in school, so they could have been friends. However, because of a troubled home life, Peter became a classic bully. Way overweight, he ate to make up for his troubled life. Where Bob was 110 to 120 pounds, Peter was at least 150 to 160 pounds, chunky, and not much taller than Bob.

For about a year, Bob tried to avoid Peter the Bully, but not always successfully. As they attended the same school, they often walked there and back at the same time. Peter would go out of his way, even cross the street, to have some fun with Bob. He would throw a bear hug, wrestle Bob to the ground, and sit on him, or sometimes just push him around and belittle him verbally. Peter was an ugly fellow, but a product of a bad home environment.

In 1958, Bob read a newspaper advertisement for Jerome Mackey's School of Martial Arts, which said *Learn judo and self-defense*. Desperate situations sometimes call for desperate gambles. For Bob, a do-or-die moment had arrived.

At the end of the 2nd World War in the Pacific in 1945 and the Korean war in 1952, some U.S. servicemen had remained in the Orient to learn the martial arts. They returned home later to teach others.

Jerome Mackey was one such person. He had studied in Japan and brought that knowledge back to the United States. His dojo, or school, was located on 56th Street and Lexington Avenue in Manhattan. The studio was on the second floor and had big windows facing Lexington Avenue, through which passers-by could see a lot of the action.

Bob was intrigued by the advertisement. This was typical 100-pound weakling stuff. The idea that you could learn to defend yourself was new to Bob. He had never heard the expression "if you want peace, prepare for war." Until then, Bob's response to a punch in the face was a question: "Why did you do that?" The need to understand can be a great hindrance sometimes.

Later, one of Bob's principles became "go all in or stay out," and reading that advertisement led to a two-year, three-day-per-week career learning martial arts. At $36 per month, Bob decided to invest his savings in the future. What he could not have known then was the great value of that knowledge for so many aspects of life: confidence, self-respect, respecting others, knowing the fragility of the human body, and wanting to do others no harm.

Jerome Mackey's school taught the Japanese style of karate known as Shotokan, as well as judo. For the first six months, Bob studied or "played" judo. Known as "the gentle way," it takes advantage of your opponent's own strength and momentum to defeat him. If they run at you, you sidestep and push them in the same direction they are already going. Isaac Newton would have been proud that his principles were being put to such good use.

Almost the entire first month consisted of doing exercises and learning how to fall, and Bob fell a lot in that time. The secret was to fall on your side, with your lower arm spread out and evenly hitting the mat with the rest of your body, thus dissipating the shock over more area. Bob quickly realized that he needed more strength, so he started lifting weights. More strength was necessary because although judo can be a beautiful ballet, it is still a grappling sport.

After six months, several fellows there were in training for the next Olympic Games. They held black belts and weighed 200 pounds or more. For a series of weeks, Bob and some of the other students became Olympic training fodder, going down on the mat constantly and becoming black and blue. They became martyrs in the search for Olympic gold. The gentle way had become the brutal way. Bob never blamed these fellows, but for self-preservation, he switched to karate, which was a non-contact sport for the most part. He learned much more, but he finally discontinued training because of a lack of funds. Within a year, he would start college and his father would pass away, but Bob's do-or-die moment had provided benefits in physical awareness, physical fitness, and self-confidence that sustained him forever. Peter the Bully had done him a great service.

As Bob played these thoughts out in his head that night, the memory of his next encounter with Peter the Bully was sweet. It had happened only three months into his training, by which time he had a completely different attitude. There was no need to understand, only to protect and have self-respect. The willingness to take a bloody nose yourself would convince bullies, who are mostly cowards, to look elsewhere.

Bob was on his way home from school at around 3 pm when Peter confronted him. Peter started his verbal abuse, but Bob fired back verbally. Bob was ready. Peter stepped in for the bear hug. Bob ducked away and started dancing to warm up and get the adrenaline flowing. He knew he had to keep moving and avoid the bear hug at all costs.

Peter came in again. Bob ducked again, and this time punched Peter in the face, sending him back in disbelief. This was not how it worked. Peter got angry and came in again. He was heavy and slow, and that was his weakness. Bob kept ducking and punching Peter in the face each time before darting away. The bear hug was dead; it didn't happen. Finally, Peter got it. In tears, he fled. Bob was jubilant but relieved. He did not know how long he could have kept up that level of action and had been worried about being caught in Peter the Bully's meat chop arms. Peter the Bully never bothered Bob again, and it got around to Bob's friends that he knew how to protect himself. Bob had many times reflected on how grateful he was that Peter the Bully had come along. Now, seven years later, he was as ready as he could be for what the next ten weeks would hold.

**Santos**

**Blam!** 5 am came again, but this time there was a difference in Barracks A. Drill Sergeant Murphy arrived and woke everyone up. Everyone, that was, except Bob. Sergeant Murphy was surprised to see one soldier standing at his bed in uniform, shaved, dressed, bed made, and ready for formation.

Murphy couldn't believe his eyes. "What's going on, soldier?"

"Nothing, Drill Sergeant. Ready for duty," Bob replied in an equally loud voice.

To not call them by their proper title would lead to instant verbal abuse. Murphy was also surprised that this first-week soldier addressed him properly, and in a booming voice that belied Bob's 120 pounds.

Bob liked to be prepared. He hated being the last one to know something or to be out of control. From that time on, he awoke at 4 am every morning without an alarm clock, an unexplainable feat. Having showered the night before, he had the huge bathroom to himself as he shaved and brushed his teeth. Next, he dressed in uniform, and at 4:30 he began to make his bed, which was difficult at first but got much easier. The first few days, he took an entire half-hour to get the hospital corners right and the top covers drum-tight. By 4:55, he was standing by his bed, relaxed and waiting for the commotion.

Drill Sergeant Richard Murphy, Jr. thought that first morning must be an aberration, but three days later, he took Bob aside and chatted with him in a surprisingly friendly voice. He wanted to understand what was going on with Bob.

"I like to be ready and I'm willing to sleep less to make it so," Bob confessed.

"Any military service?" Murphy asked.

Bob mentioned the two years of ROTC training. Aha! Murphy now understood why Bob knew how to address him properly.

The next day, Murphy cajoled Bob into becoming the barracks leader as well as squad leader for one of the four squads of the platoon. He appealed to Bob's military knowledge and explained that the next nine weeks were about learning leadership and that Bob might as well begin right there. Bob accepted, and so began a challenging and exciting nine weeks. Squad leadership involved many things, including ensuring the trainees in his squad got out of the barracks on time, making sure the beds were made, and verbally reporting the squad's presence at morning formation, as well as leading some parade ground marches.

"1st Squad all present and accounted for, Drill Sergeant," Bob reported in a loud booming voice the next morning at formation.

"Now, that is how to make a report," Sergeant Murphy announced to the trainees.

Bob liked his newfound status, although he was now working at 90% of capacity instead of just 75%, where he liked to be. Not everything was rosy, however, as Bob found out quickly. One of the men in the barracks, a headstrong fellow named Raphale Santos, decided to test him.

It was about 5 pm, just before dinner, and Bob was asking his fellow barracks mates to keep the showers cleaner. "We have got to do a better job," he said. "Dripping faucets, dirty towels lying around, filthy floor. These things have to stop. The drill sergeants are just looking for reasons to make our lives even more miserable."

Santos, who didn't like being told what to do by anybody, sized up Bob as a smaller guy and decided to move. He walked up and got into Bob's face, obviously looking for a fight.

"Who made you God?" he demanded.

Bob had known that someone would test him. The fact that Santos was bigger and heavier was actually a good thing. *If I can get past him, the others will just fall into line,* he thought.

Inches apart, Bob provoked Santos. "Look, if you can't follow instructions, you'll never make it here. You might as well pack up and leave now."

As Bob knew he would, Santos waded in for a knockout punch. Having seen him handle his rifle, Bob knew Santos was right-handed, so he predicted Santos would come in and throw a left hand to get his attention and then follow up with the right. Bob knew he also had to end it quickly, without letting Santos get any real punches in. He was no match for Santos' power. As Santos threw his left, Bob stepped back just out of range and grabbed both of Santos' arms by his shirt. Pulling and twisting slightly to get Santos one-footed on his left foot, Bob twisted to the right and used his own left foot to sweep Santos' left foot out from under him. Crash! down they went to the barracks floor with Bob on top. A basic judo throw called Osoto-Gari.

They continued grappling for a while, then, as if by prearranged signal, they both decided to stop. Bob had made his point and was happy Santos was not crushed. He was not trying to make enemies.

The other trainees got the message that Bob was willing to fight to keep the group safe, and Santos kept his "face" by not being beaten. Several of them dropped by Bob's bunk to tell him he had handled himself well. Later that night, Bob went over to Santos' bunk, and they spoke briefly. Santos was a headstrong guy who did not want to be ordered around, but he was willing to do the right thing too.

"It's hard being here," he said. "We are all wondering if we are heading to Vietnam, and that makes us a little angry."

"You are right," Bob said. "We are all feeling that way."

Bob suggested they work together to keep Barracks A orderly for the next nine weeks. Santos agreed, and a partnership was formed that lasted the duration of basic training. Bob slept well that night, knowing that the next nine weeks were on a good track.

**Bronx Zoo**

In 1958, Bob was fourteen years old and in high school. The phone rang. Bob was slow to answer because he didn't want to deliver fish that day. He worked for his uncle Warner, the best fish man in the Bronx. Probably the best in New York City. The money was good. At 25 cents per order plus tips, he could earn $15 in three or four hours on a busy day. His savings would be put to good use the next year for judo lessons. But it was not Uncle Warner on the phone. It was Bob's friend, Bill.

"There is a new baby elephant at the Bronx Zoo, and we can get in for free on Sunday," Bill said. "Do you want in?"

"Sure," Bob said. "Sounds like fun and I haven't been to the zoo in forever."

Bob was working hard in his first year of high school. After school, he would either work in the fish store or help out with chores at home while his mom worked at Ohrbach's Department Store in Manhattan. Bob would also spend some time with his dad, who had been sick for five years. With a tumor near his spinal cord, where it was basically inoperable, Jake was almost always in pain.

Sunday came and Bob, Bill, and two other friends headed for the Bronx Zoo. They took the bus on the Grand Concourse and changed at Fordham Road for the bus that dropped you right at the zoo entrance. After walking around for an hour, seeing the birds, the seals, and the amazing polar bears, they went in search of the new baby elephant, whose name was Bubba. Bubba was three months old and sticking close to his mom, but he was eager to play and stuck his trunk into anything he could find.

They say there are 40,000 muscles in the elephant's trunk alone, compared with 639 muscles in the whole human body. Bob could never figure out how they got that thing under control.

At about 2 pm, the gang of four decided to start the trip home to get back in time for supper. Only something went wrong. As they approached the path to the exit, a gang of about six or seven tough kids came walking toward them but had not yet seen them.

The four took cover, not wanting to confront the tough kids. Bill acted quickly and got on another path to another exit, but Bob and the others remained hiding behind some bushes, out of sight, waiting for the tough kids to pass by. It seemed to take forever, but the threat blew over when the bad guys departed along the path. Then, more relaxed now, the friends came out from their hiding place and walked down yet another path.

"Looks like it's all good now," Bob said to the others.

While on their way to the exit, they encountered another group of five of their friends just arriving at the zoo. As it was a warm day and they now had larger numbers than the tough kids, Bob and his two friends decided to join the newcomers and stay a while longer. Unfortunately for Bob, he got home very late, at about 9 pm. His mother had gotten worried and called Bill's mom, who'd said, "Yes, Bill is home. He doesn't know where Bob is because a gang of toughs came by and they all separated."

That was the wrong message for Sarah and Jake to hear. There was nothing they could do but worry. When Bob returned home, he got the beating of his life for making them so worried.

In the barracks, Bob finally fell asleep with his memories.

**Last Weeks of Training**

The next few weeks fell into a routine. Up at 5 am and into formation. A six-mile walk, interspersed with running, with a backpack, followed by breakfast at the mess hall. Next, instruction in some topic of the basic training program.

Weapons training was a main part of the training. Each trainee was issued an M1 rifle. The M1 rifle was the standard weapon for infantry soldiers in World War II and Korea, and it saw duty during Vietnam too. It was replaced by the M14 Rifle in 1965.

The M1 is a.30-caliber, gas-operated, eight-shot, clip-fed, semi-automatic rifle. It is 43.6 inches long and weighs 9.5 pounds. It has an iron sightline with a rear aperture sight that can be calibrated for accuracy at 100 to 500 yards.

Although largely replaced in Vietnam, it is a sturdy weapon and great for training. At 9.5 pounds, it is a formidable weight to hold steady while sighting a target and firing, not to mention carrying it on a forced march of six to seven miles. Not everyone could handle it.

A few of the battalion had some difficulties, both physically and emotionally. The physical challenge of the

M1 added to the stress. The trainees who fell by the wayside came to be known by the drill sergeants as "the sick, the lame, and the lazy." No one wanted to become part of that group, so the trainees became harder and tougher over those next few weeks.

Besides its weight, the M1 has a big disadvantage for left-handed soldiers. While the clip feeds from the top, the bolt action is on the right side of the stock. Each time a round is fired, the shell casing ejects from the right side, scaring the hell out of left-handers.

Bob, being left-handed, got hit in the face by hot shell casings several times until he figured a way to adjust by leaning back just a touch. Furthermore, the bolt action had to be driven back at times to manually eject a shell casing or a shell, or to put in a new clip.

For a left-hander, handling the bolt action was a devilish dance. Bob's solution was to reach across the barrel with his left hand, push the bolt to the rear, and duck the shell casing at the same time. Not something you would want to do in battle. The M1, although fearsome, was essentially a right-handed weapon.

"This is your weapon. Eat with it, sleep with it. Learn how it works inside and out. Take it apart and put it back together. It will save your life." This was the mantra drilled into their heads every morning at the firing range.

At the firing range, there were large rectangular tables under a tent canvas. Classes in breaking down and reassembling the M1 were given there. In the jungles of Vietnam, there was water, humidity, and above all, mud. If you couldn't disassemble, clean, and reassemble an M1 quickly, your life expectancy was low.

"Faster, faster. Is that the best you can do? You'll be dead in no time out there," was the drill sergeant's message in his rightful effort to save the trainees' lives.

After the classes, the trainees fired the M1 at circular targets 100 to 300 yards away. At each session, they fired eight clips, or ninety-six rounds, of 30.06 ammo.

"All ready on the left, all ready on the right, all ready on the firing range," called out one of the weapons instructors.

Bang, bang, bang! The sound of the bullets firing and the smell of the gunpowder enveloped them. They began to feel like real soldiers, but scared too, knowing where they might be headed. Weeks of training did two things. They trained everyone to fire an M1, and they separated them into categories: expert, marksman, or ordinary, which was no designation at all.

Bob, being left-handed, struggled with the M1, but he eventually made peace with it and achieved a marksman rating, getting a badge for his dress uniform. He was reminded of a college chemistry class in which he had struggled to make the beakers, pipettes, flasks, and the rest work together to get a reliable experimental result.

One of his chemistry professors had told him something that had made a difference and allowed him to succeed.

"Bob, there are only two options. You will master this equipment or this equipment will master you. So get to it."

Another forced march back to the barracks, clean and store the rifles, and head for the mess hall for lunch. Having already burned thousands of breakfast calories, everyone wanted more.

Chipped beef on toast, or "shit on a shingle" as it has been known in the military since around 1935, served with a creamy white sauce, braised beef, fried chicken, mashed potatoes and gravy, vegetable soup, hamburgers, French fries. They couldn't get enough. Apple pie and coffee for dessert.

After lunch, they got back in formation and headed for the theater for the afternoon's training film. Hygiene, battle tactics, military law. Every subject under the sun. The puzzling thing was why the movie theaters were kept so warm. After getting up at 5 am, twelve miles of hiking, and a big lunch, half the men in the theater would instantly fall asleep. Within ten minutes, the theater became a weird, other-worldly concert hall, the snoring so loud, you wondered how anyone could sleep through it or how the base commander could allow it.

In those middle weeks, the drill sergeants kept up the pressure.

"Faster, better, earlier, address me properly." They prodded and pushed until they were hated by all. By week six, Bob and the rest could not imagine a worse fate than continuing in basic training. Even fighting in the remote jungles of Vietnam must be better, they thought.

In the sixth week, a blood drive was held. At morning formation, it was announced that anyone donating blood could skip afternoon PT. Bob, Tom, and many others were skeptical. Some old sayings had to exist for a reason. Like "never volunteer." They hung back, but many donated, looking forward to an easy afternoon, but Bob's philosophy was "never be lazy, always have more gas in the tank, and never run out of bullets."

The morning was physically hard, as expected. At afternoon formation, the reveal occurred. Some of the trainees called in their chit.

"I gave blood this morning, so I would like to skip PT as was promised," Matt from Staten Island said.

Drill Sergeant Murphy laughed out loud. "Get out of PT? What did you give, soldier? A gallon?"

The rest of the blood donors all got the message and remained with the group to face their daily afternoon hardships.

The battalion mastered the six-mile hike, sometimes double-time, sometimes not. The forced marches got easier with repetition, and by week seven many chants were sung, led by the drill sergeants or the squad leaders. The chants were sung to the cadence of the movement and were the soul of the march. By week seven, after three miles of the six, the battalion would enter a collective trance.

"It was as if we had been marching forever, and would always be marching," Bob said.

The left and right feet moved inexorably to the ground, one after the other, keeping the rhythm.

*Your lay-eft, your lay-eft, your lay-eft, right, lay-eft.*

*I don't know but I believe,*

*that I'm going home on Christmas leave.*

*Sound off 1, 2; sound off 3, 4.*

*Break it on down, 1, 2, 3, 4; 1, 2… 3, 4.*

Then, as if a season of the year had turned the page, week eight brought a dramatic change. Miraculously, the battalion became a cohesive unit. Trainees followed instructions instantly, kept in formation, and lived the soldiers' life gracefully and without complaint. Life became easier. The drill sergeants became less abusive and more friendly. Their job was done. A mass realization of this metamorphosis occurred, and hatred turned to love. The trainees got it. They loved the drill sergeants, and the drill sergeants loved them back. The harassment game was over. With two weeks left, Vietnam came back into focus as the main worry.

On March 26, 1966, nine months earlier, the first large-scale anti-war demonstrations had taken place in dozens of American cities. In New York City, 20,000 Americans marched down Fifth Avenue after a rally in Central Park.

2,000 protesters marched down State Street in Chicago, and protests took place in Boston, Washington, Oklahoma City, Atlanta, and other cities as well.

By 1965, a major escalation of the Vietnam War by the U.S. had begun. Operation Rolling Thunder was an aerial bombardment of North Vietnam, which continued until November 1968. Rolling Thunder was an attempt to get the North Vietnamese to the bargaining table without pouring more men into Vietnam. On June 29, 1966, U.S. planes bombed Hanoi and Haiphong, major population centers, for the first time. The goal was to limit the flow of men and supplies from the north to the south by crippling transportation systems and North Vietnam's industrial base.

At Fort Jackson's PX in the afternoon that week, the trainees hung out and chatted. Several times per week they could stock up on junk food and make sure they got something from each of the four junk food groups for healthy eating. Matt Sachs, from Staten Island, talked about becoming an airborne medic.

"Matt, that is a scary thought. That would be like doing two daredevil acts simultaneously. Like Evel Knievel flying across a canyon while escaping from manacles like Houdini," Bob remarked. "How can you even consider that?"

"You know Bob, I have always wanted to prove myself and never had the chance until now," Matt replied.

Bob, taken aback, had no such grand designs of his own. He wanted to serve his country and get back home. Some others talked about home, going back to school, back to a job, or to their girl when they got out.

The jukebox was blaring, and they settled into the music and ate some red Twizzlers. The sound of the Mamas and Papas hit single "Monday, Monday" permeated the PX. Next up was the amazingly popular Motown sound of the Supremes' "You Can't Hurry Love." And later, the even more famous "Stop in the Name of Love."

The lovefest continued. One evening in week eight, after a long day of training, the battalion fell into formation just before dinner.

Drill Sergeant Major Jaimee Dominguez spoke to the men. "You men should be proud of your achievements in the last eight weeks. But be careful out there next week. Don't do anything crazy or your training could be wasted."

After reminding them of his "two years of civilian education," he began an exercise before dinner.

"Let me see the hands of those who have a Ph.D. or a master's degree," he said. One or two hands went up. "I want you to go around the barracks and mess hall and pick up any cigar butts you see."

The two broke out of formation and began.

"Let me see your hands if you have a college degree," Dominguez continued. Many hands went up, including

Bob's and Tom's. "I want you to walk around and pick up all the cigarette butts you see."

Everyone was struggling to hold in a chuckle.

"Who has a high school diploma?" Dominguez asked. Still more hands went up. "I want you to go and pick up any pieces of paper or candy wrappers."

There were now only thirty or forty trainees left standing in formation – those without a high school diploma.

"For the rest of you, I want you to stand around here, watch these guys, and get an education," Drill Sergeant Major Dominguez said.

The barracks and mess hall grounds were spotless, and the trainees were roaring with laughter at dinner. All part of the lovefest. And so things went in basic training at Fort Jackson, South Carolina, in the fall and winter of 1966.

For this group of trainees, week nine was Christmas leave and then a return to finish week ten. Christmas came and went. Bob went home and made the most he could of the week. He knew a beautiful girl named Marie McDonald, whom he had met four years earlier when he'd worked evenings at St. Luke's Hospital in Upper Manhattan. Bob had called Marie from Fort Jackson and invited her to a Broadway show. Gwen Verdon was starring in "Sweet Charity," a story of a dancer for hire working at a Times Square dance hall.

It was a brilliant musical, choreographed for Broadway by Bob Fosse. It won the Tony Award that year for best choreography and had 608 performances before closing in July. Marie was a bit older, and there was no hope of a relationship, but spending time with her felt good to Bob.

*A future military hero walking arm in arm with a beautiful woman down Broadway in New York City on Friday night,* Bob thought. *It doesn't get better.*

Sarah and Henry were glad to see Bob, as were his friends. An accident or unfortunate event that would cause him to miss basic training graduation was unacceptable, so Bob was cautious, spending most of the time hanging out with family in a quiet week. Bob's friends were keen to hear about his adventures beyond the Bronx. They marveled at the stories of life away from the pavement. Most had draft deferments of one kind or another – for graduate school, marriage, or medical reasons – and so would not have a similar experience.

Precisely one week later, Bob arrived back at Fort Jackson for the final week or so of basic training. The last days were uneventful. The training went smoothly, and anticipation was in the air. Orders for their next assignment would arrive soon. The battalion would be split up and sent in many directions, never to meet again. You did not want to be sent to Fort Polk, Louisiana, which was renowned for its advanced infantry and jungle training. Everyone knew Fort Polk was a ten-week stopover on the way to Vietnam.

It was January in South Carolina. The days were mostly bright and sunny, but the temperature went on a wild ride every day, from 35 degrees at 5 am to 65 degrees at 1 pm. To stay warm enough, you had to put on all your layers to fall out into formation at 5 am. You hoped for a quick trip to the barracks before lunch so you could take off a layer or two. Without this de-layering, you were sweating bullets by 2 pm during the long march.

The last day of training arrived in mid-January. Time to say goodbyes and turn in supplies. Beds were left unmade, but sheets and pillowcases were folded neatly on them.

Military orders are a jumble of letters and numbers. They are not secret, but they are in a code all of their own that few people can decipher. All Bob could make out was that he was on his way to Fort Gordon, Georgia, in Augusta. So far so good: not Fort Polk. He would not know until later that he had been promoted to private first class, one stripe on his sleeve, or of the award of the marksman medal.

After dinner, the soldiers packed up and headed for the bus stop. Dress greens were the travel uniform, and the whole group looked great, looked military. Black shoes, spit-shined so you could see your face. Brass lapel pins polished to a high shine with Brasso on their dress green jackets. Campaign caps on their heads. They were headed they knew not where to do they knew not what, but they were ready, molded into soldiers in only ten short weeks. Ready to go!

Bob's bus arrived late, pulled into the station, and made a loud screeching sound followed by a hiss like a huge animal exhaling when it came to a stop. The driver got out, used the convenience, and brought back a Tab and a deli sandwich. A half-hour later, Bob and thirty-four others scrambled aboard the bus for the trip to Fort Gordon. Green duffel bags with military ID numbers stenciled on them neatly stowed. That number would follow you wherever you went in the U.S. Army.

It was already 10 pm, so they would arrive at Fort Gordon late. The huge Continental Trailways bus exited the depot slowly, made the short hop to the highway, merged onto U.S. Route 20, and skirted Columbia to the northwest. From there, it was a straight shot to the southwest for about an hour and a half to Fort Gordon. Many of the soldiers grabbed some sleep, but Bob wasn't tired. He sat back and let his mind wander over the past ten weeks, his past life, and what his future, spelled out in those unknowable orders, would hold.

# Chapter Two – Fort Gordon and Augusta, Georgia

While on the bus to Fort Gordon, Bob thought about the past ten weeks. He felt lucky he was in great physical shape and knew some martial arts. That had already helped him, and he hoped his luck would continue.

The thought of physical fitness took him back to 1952.

**Friday Night Fights**

Before Bob's dad fell sick, he worked for the U.S. Army as a civilian employee at Fort Jay on Governors Island. After commuting all week, two hours each way, Jake was always tired on Friday evenings. But Jake, Bob, and Henry would hang out together and watch the Friday Night Fights. Jake was off from work on Saturday and Sunday, and Bob and Henry had no school, so Friday night was their time to hang out. After dinner, they would settle in the living room and watch TV on their recently purchased Admiral 12" table model TV. As usual, Jake had borrowed the money from Citibank, but the payments were easy and the TV was a priceless gift to his sons.

The Gillette Cavalcade of Sports sponsored the incredible Friday Night Fights, where Bob got to see the best fighters of the day while hanging with his family. Sugar Ray Robinson; Emile Griffith; Gaspar Ortega, who was a real crowd favorite; Floyd Patterson; Ingemar Johansson; Rocky Marciano; and Jersey Joe Walcott appeared, among many others. The fights were broadcast live from Madison Square Garden from 1946 to 1960.

Bob thought back to September 23, 1952. Sarah always made a special dish on Fridays. That Friday, it was brisket, green beans, and roasted potatoes with a brown gravy from the brisket. Dinner for four was always nice on Friday nights, when Jake didn't have to worry about getting up for work. He always asked his boys about their studies and how they were doing. He liked this better than being brought in by Sarah to put out a fire after something had gone wrong.

Dinner over and the dishes washed, Jake and the two boys headed into the living room and turned on the TV. They were all anticipating the championship fight between Rocky Marciano and Jersey Joe Walcott, the defending heavyweight champion.

At precisely 9:30, the show started and the fight got underway.

Marciano and Walcott were both right-handed, so their movements were like a ballet of titans as they stepped clockwise around the ring. In the first few rounds, Marciano was knocked down for the first time ever.

"Wow," Bob said. "Look at that. Unbelievable."

Marciano got up at a five-count and was back in the fight.

Then it was a long slog of even performance through the end of the twelfth round, the two fighters circling each other in the clockwise ballet. Both fighters looked exhausted. Jake had watched a lot of fights and was a big Marciano fan.

"Guys, you watch. Marciano is undefeated and Walcott is older," he said. "These last few rounds will belong to Marciano."

The referee rang the bell and the 13th round started. After a couple of minutes, Rocky Marciano caught Walcott with a right to the jaw and knocked him out. The referee held up Marciano's hand and said the anticipated words. "And the *new* heavyweight champion of the world."

Sitting on the bus approaching Fort Gordon that night, those memories meant the world to Bob.

**Fort Gordon**

The giant Continental Trailways bus pulled off the highway and made the last lap into Fort Gordon, arriving at the depot around midnight. As the bus entered through the main gate, everyone looked left. A huge sign was suspended 200 feet in the air, supported by tall telephone poles. The sign was in bold, block-style lettering that said *A soldier must first train for combat, anything else is bullshit…*

Bob swallowed hard. "OK, I guess we have arrived."

With a loud shuddering noise, the front door opened as the huge bus came to a stop. The thirty-five soldiers, now wide awake, filed slowly off the bus and picked up their duffel bags from the underside storage compartment. Standing about five yards away were two non-commissioned officers – a sergeant and a corporal. Still, no one knew what their orders said, and it soon became plain that these two non-coms did not understand the orders either.

"Welcome to Fort Gordon," the sergeant said. "We want to get you accustomed to life here, so follow me now with your duffel bags."

So, at midnight, he led the thirty-five newly minted soldiers in their dress green uniforms to a training field and put them through a hard training session.

Fort Gordon was home to several important U.S. Army training facilities: Advanced Airborne Infantry School, Signal School, Military Police School, and a base hospital that was a major receiving station for wounded soldiers returning from Vietnam.

Originally founded during World War I, Fort Gordon was named in honor of John Brown Gordon, a major general in the Confederate Army, a Georgia governor, a U.S. Senator, and a businessman.

Going through the monkey bars in dress greens at midnight, Bob and everyone else assumed they were headed for the infantry, not even knowing it would be the Airborne Infantry. Fortunately for Bob and six others, after about ten minutes of bone-banging exercise, another noncom arrived. He was higher ranking, a sergeant first class, who it turned out could read orders. After reviewing all thirty-five orders, the sergeant first class separated Bob and six others. The other twenty-eight soldiers were indeed headed for advanced infantry training. Bob and the six had a brighter future, it seemed. Still not knowing what that future would be, the seven breathed a collective sigh of relief. Whatever it was to be, it had to be an improvement.

The seven soldiers were given temporary quarters for the night, to be reassigned somewhere on Fort Gordon in the morning. Soon, Bob would learn to read orders himself. He would see that the lucky seven all had something in common. They were all college graduates and had all scored highly on the various intelligence tests taken right after induction. They were to be assigned to permanent jobs at Fort Gordon and given on-the-job training. In its wisdom, the U.S. Army saw the benefit of putting these soldiers to work immediately without spending any more money to train them.

Morning came. After a big breakfast at the mess hall, Bob and the others arrived at the reassignment office. A couple of hours later, after all the paperwork was done, they were reassigned to the four corners of the base – a couple to the Signal School, a couple to the Airborne Infantry School, a couple to Base Administration, and Bob drew the assignment to the U.S. Army hospital, a small 250-bed hospital that was rapidly increasing in importance as more and more wounded soldiers returned from Vietnam.

The seven had all been placed in the TRAPP program, as listed on their orders. That meant "Train and Retain as Permanent Party," or in other words, "put them to work immediately and train them on the job." Because the army needed some smart people to make all the gears work, these seven were diverted from the Vietnam pipeline, the giant stream of soldiers being trained and sent directly to Vietnam. Bob and the others felt lucky. They still could not know the future, but at that moment they felt lucky.

Bob showed up for work at the hospital, an aging two-story wooden building on the northern side of the base, and was given a desk and a set of army manuals that provided the bulk of his on-the-job training. He learned how to complete a wide variety of HR actions, including leaves of absence, reassignments, and promotions. He became an expert in reading and creating military orders. With this knowledge, he learned that he had been promoted to PFC, private first class, and had gotten a marksman badge in basic training.

**The Hospital at Fort Gordon**

Because of the ramp-up in the war, the U.S. Army had to increase the number of hospital beds for the wounded returning to the U.S.

At fiscal year-end 1966, there were just under 15,000 hospital beds in Class I and Class II hospitals in CONUS (continental U.S.). Class II hospitals were larger and better equipped to treat more illnesses. Today, they are known as general hospitals. By the end of 1967, the number of beds had increased about 25% to more than 18,000 beds.

In addition, even some smaller hospitals like the one at Fort Gordon with only a couple of hundred beds were upgraded to Class I. The rapidly increasing numbers of wounded soldiers returning simply required more beds. Fort Gordon, in Augusta Georgia, was also geographically important, being located in the southeast, the home of many of these soldiers. The army's policy was to have the wounded treated in a hospital as close to their homes as possible.

In 1967, "utilization and requirements" studies were being conducted to determine what upgrades a hospital needed. The study for Fort Gordon was just getting underway, and Bob's new boss, Sergeant Wilfred Miller, told him, "You are the perfect person to handle it."

This hospital was already almost full to capacity with wounded returnees from the First Air Cavalry and the First Infantry Division, among other units. Later that year, after the upgrades, Fort Gordon was designated a Class I hospital as part of the CONUS hospital system.

After a few days, Bob was settled into his new home at Barracks B, just off Avenue of the States, near Barton Field. He walked the ten minutes up Rice Road and across Chamberlain Avenue to his job at the hospital. Five minutes in the other direction was the mess hall, the PX, bowling alley, and library. That was to be the perimeter of his life for the next four and a half months, and he accepted it.

In the barracks, his bunk neighbor was a fellow named Phil Reeder from Queens, New York. Phil had just transferred back from Europe and was finishing the last six months of his army service at Fort Gordon. He was a sergeant, AG Division, assigned to administration at the MP school. Phil was in good physical shape, about 25 years old, with a roundish face and short sandy hair. He had a good sense of humor and a ready smile. The U.S. Army had not hurt him at all. Bob and Phil became friends and traveled to town together many times for a burger or pizza. Bob, who had never owned a car, felt lucky that Phil had one.

Matt Sachs of Staten Island, one of the fellows from basic training, was living at one of the barracks at the advanced infantry training school. Bob saw him a few times during those few months. Matt had gotten his wish and was in the Airborne Infantry Training school, so he was often unavailable to hang out with. He was later to complete his airborne training at Fort Benning, and then qualify as an airborne medic. As Matt had said, he had his own agenda, had something to prove to himself, and he'd picked a heck of a way to do it. Bob never saw him or spoke with him again after Fort Gordon, but Matt was often in his thoughts.

In the adjacent barracks were two of the seven college grads. They would accompany Bob in his travels over the next year and a half – Charles Weitz of Queens, New York, and Peter Ingrassia of Lake Placid, New York. The three had similar educational backgrounds and would share a similar experience for the next year and a half.

Augusta, Georgia, is a small town located on the Savannah River, a 301-mile-long river that starts in the southeastern side of the Appalachian Mountains and finally empties into the Atlantic Ocean at Savannah. The river forms the main border between Georgia and South Carolina. Augusta's main geological feature is its location on the Fall Line, a jagged line running across middle Georgia from Macon to Augusta, marking the dividing line between the rolling Piedmont to the north and the flat Coastal Plain to the south. The rapid descent of the terrain toward the Coastal Plain causes a number of waterfalls in the rivers that cross it.

Augusta was named after the mother of King George III of England and established in 1736. In 1960, it had about 70,000 residents. Today, it has just under 200,000 residents and is famous for hosting the Masters Golf Tournament since 1934. It became home to the military in 1941, when Camp Gordon was opened just a few days after the bombing of Pearl Harbor. Today, Fort Gordon is Augusta's largest employer with just under 20,000 employees.

Phil Reeder had been on base for a couple of months and had bought a beautiful 1965 steely blue Oldsmobile Cutlass 4-4-2. The official Oldsmobile color was Lucerne Mist. This model of Cutlass became a model in its own right from 1968 to 1971 but reverted back to an option through the mid-1970s. This particular car had a 400 cubic inch engine, two-speed automatic transmission, 4-barrel carburetor, and dual exhausts. Although the 4-4-2 did designate a four-speed transmission, it was a manual transmission. It also had an optional two-speed automatic transmission but still proudly displayed the "4-4-2" badge. The interior had a white vinyl top and black flooring. Phil had bought it, with only 26,000 miles on the odometer, from the original owner in Augusta for a low price. The challenge was that the car always looked like it was traveling ten miles per hour faster than it was, so Phil had to drive slowly.

"Hey, why don't we head downtown and grab some Pizza at Arturo's?" Phil asked Bob one afternoon.

"That sounds great. I am ready to bust out of here," Bob said.

"In the two weeks you have been here, you haven't once said that. Why didn't you say something?"

"I know," Bob said. "I am well aware I don't have wheels and haven't wanted to mention it."

Their workday usually ended at 5 pm. At 6 pm, Phil and Bob got into the blue Cutlass. Phil revved the engine, and it sounded great. Vrooom, Vrooom, and off they went, moving slowly off the base, a short hop to local Route 1, then to Route 28 for the six miles to Broad Street in the old town. Going slowly in Augusta was smart. The police didn't have much to do, and as a soldier and an outsider, you did not want to be the one to provide them with excitement. They arrived at Broad Street, and Phil found a parking spot right in front of Arturo's. It was Thursday night and not crowded. Most of the soldiers would go out on the town Friday or Saturday night, but not so much on Thursdays. Most streets, including Broad, had diagonal parking. You just slid into the spot and you were done.

"Amazing how easy it is to park compared with parallel parking in the South Bronx," Bob commented.

They sat down, ordered a large, crispy pizza to share and Tabs to drink. Phil was smart. He did not want to drink and drive. A low profile around Augusta was the way to go.

"Let's enjoy Augusta, but not screw it up," Phil said.

Phil talked a little about Queens, and Bob talked some about the South Bronx. South Bronx was less affluent, but Bob's stories about the Yankee Stadium captured Phil's interest. The jukebox was blaring, and the music was great. The song playing was The Mamas & The Papas hit single, "Creek Alley," from their just-released hit album, *The Mamas & The Papas Deliver*.

The Mamas & The Papas had become a sensation the previous year with "California Dreaming" and were well appreciated in the South Bronx, where kids like Bob and his friends had no way to escape the cold winter.

Motown was still crazy popular, and soul was coming into its own. Atlantic Records had released Wilson Pickett's album, *Wicked Pickett*, in June 1966. From this album, the single "Mustang Sally" continued to be played on the jukeboxes. Augusta was also the home of James Brown, who entertained the troops from time to time. Bob was soon to learn how popular soul music was about to become in Europe.

The pizza arrived just as ordered. The cheese was still melting and dripped off their lips. They washed down the pizza with ice-cold Tabs.

"Man, I feel good," Bob said to Phil and the jukebox and anyone else in earshot.

They talked about the future. Phil said he was going to return to Queen, NY, where his parents lived. "I'll move into Manhattan and go into filmmaking. I hear there is this happening area called Tribeca where film people are moving in."

Bob didn't know what he would do, so he simply thanked Phil for taking him to town. "Thanks for this outing. I feel a little lost here in a small town, especially without a driver's license. In the South Bronx, I never needed one."

"You know, Bob, you should get one while you are here," Phil said. Showing his good nature, he added, "You can use my car to practice and then take the driver's test."

Bob was surprised but elated and grateful. He told Phil about his practice sessions and near-death experiences learning to drive a stick shift BMW in the South Bronx.

After an hour, Phil said, "That was good, man. Shall we?"

"Sure," Bob replied.

"Why don't we walk around the block, then head back?"

They walked past an ice cream parlor, but were too full to indulge. Besides, they knew they could get something at the PX on the base. They got back in the car and reversed the trip, traveling slowly to the base in the steely blue Cutlass.

That night, on his bunk, Bob thought back to the time at home in the Bronx, just before he was drafted, when he'd learned to drive.

**Learning to Drive a Stick Shift**

At 22 years old, Bob still had no driver's license, partly because of the lack of money to buy a car, but also because life in the South Bronx didn't require it. Furthermore, a car would require a place to park, another difficulty in this dense area of the South Bronx. So Bob used buses and trains like everyone else. However, a friend who lived in a less crowded area had recently bought a BMW and offered to teach Bob how to drive. Rich had not planned to go to college and was working, so he could afford a nice car.

The car was a 1965 BMW 2000, a white two-door sedan featuring wide taillights, a lot of trim, and four round individual headlights.

They would meet early on Saturdays, and Rich would drive to Hunts Point, a commercial area with wide streets and little traffic. It was just a fifteen-minute drive on the Cross Bronx Expressway to the Bronx River Parkway South, to the Bruckner Expressway, and then to Hunts Point Avenue. As soon as Rich made the turn onto Hunts Point Avenue, he would turn the car over to Bob.

The BMW was a stick shift, however, and they were some scary rides. Bob was learning street signs, driving rules, driving sense, and at the same time struggling with the stick shift. Bob would drive down Hunts Point Avenue, turn left onto Halleck Street, a nice wide street at Hunts Point Market, turn left on Randall Ave, and around again on Oak Point Avenue back to Halleck. Any left turn was life-threatening as Bob had to watch the other cars, traffic lights, and the cross-traffic, and simultaneously downshift and wait to make the left.

Thus, left turns were the gold standard of how you were doing. They reached DEFCON 3 several times, and the life-saving fallback was Bob shifting into neutral and slamming on the brakes. They took a gamble on the final Saturday, and Bob drove out of Hunts Point and home. At Southern Boulevard, a major Bronx thoroughfare, even a right turn was hard, and again the brakes got slammed. Not great for the car, but Bob and Rich lived to tell the tale. A couple of months of these nerve-racking rides left Bob with fairly good road sense, several near-death experiences, and some great stories to tell, but unfortunately no driver's license. What Bob couldn't have known then was that he had learned a lot, enough to be a decent driver in an automatic shift car.

He lay in his bunk in Augusta and drifted off to sleep.

**Driving in Augusta**

The next day, Bob and Phil took the Cutlass out for a practice session, with Bob driving around the base. The ride was smooth, and Phil saw that his car was not at risk. Bob's near-death experiences with the stick shift BMW had prepared him to sit back, relax and enjoy the ride in an automatic. So, after four practice runs in two weeks, they decided to head downtown so Bob could take the driver's test.

A prior phone call to the Richmond County sheriff's office had confirmed that no appointment was necessary. "Just show up between 9 am and 5 pm to take the driver's test," the person at the other end of the phone said.

The sheriff's office was located downtown, not far from Arturo's. Phil drove, slowly as usual, and pulled up to the sheriff's office at 9:30 in the morning. It was a spring morning, filled with sunshine, and sure to be a day to remember for Bob.

Now, just to set record straight, in order to get a driver's license in the South Bronx, you had to do the following: fill out a form requesting the driver's test, wait about two weeks to receive a test date, go over to the DMV, take the written test, and then wait another two weeks to get the results. Once you had the results, you filled out another form requesting a road test, then you waited another two weeks to be given a road test date. Then you went to the test center and took the road test. Then you had to then wait another two weeks for the results. Then and only then would you get a driver's license. "In New York City, they should have monuments erected to those who died while patiently waiting for a driver's license," Bob joked.

In Augusta, it was a little different. In the sheriff's office, Bob walked over to a window behind which a sheriff's deputy sat. After exchanging pleasantries, Bob explained why he was there. The officer came out from behind the window with a booklet in his hand.

He took Bob to one of three small booths on the side of the room and said, "Please take this test and return it to me when you are done."

Bob completed the written test consisting of twenty-five multiple-choice questions in about twenty minutes and returned it to the deputy. So far so good.

"What happens next?" Bob asked the deputy.

"Just give me a couple of minutes," the deputy said. He sat down and graded the test, which took exactly two minutes, then came out from behind the window and said, "Let's go." Bob looked puzzled. "Let's go take the road test," the deputy clarified.

Bob couldn't believe this was happening, but he went outside with the deputy. He introduced him to Phil, who was sitting in the Cutlass. Bob and the deputy got in the car, Bob in the driver's seat, the deputy in the front passenger seat, and Phil shuffled to the back seat.

The deputy guided Bob through the road test. Bob backed out the diagonally parked Cutlass, switched to drive, and drove around the block, making four right turns at four stop signs. He parked diagonally in the same parking spot in front of the sheriff's office.

The deputy got out of the car and said, "Bob, come on inside with me."

While Bob waited at the glass window, the deputy went back to his desk, filled out a driver's license, and handed it to Bob. "Here you go. Congratulations, Bob."

So, in a total time of about one hour, Bob had an official Georgia State driver's license and was legal to drive from that moment.

Bob was elated. He hugged Phil, then they drove back to the base – Bob driving – and celebrated with hamburgers and ice-cold Tabs. A day to remember!

Although it happened in the space of one hour, it took a long time for the importance of the driver's license to sink in. Not only was this license crucial for Bob's next eighteen months, but something he had not done in 22 years in the South Bronx had been accomplished in one hour in the little town of Augusta, Georgia. Bob saw that there was a whole wide world out there where all things were possible, and he suddenly realized that he could exit the Bronx.

As spring progressed toward summer and the temperature got warmer, drives in the country were a frequent pastime. Aiken, South Carolina, was a great local destination, about 32 miles northeast of Fort Gordon and easy to get to. Phil allowed Bob to drive several times, and Bob got very comfortable with the rules of the road. It was a quick hop to Route 78, then to Route 520, the beltway around Augusta to the southeast, and back on Route 78 to Aiken. They would sometimes stop at Gloverville Pond to watch the ducks for a bit, then head into Aiken, a very scenic, small town that earlier had become a wintering spot for the rich. There were large tracts of farmland and very large estates, some of which had been cotton plantations. Bob could enjoy being in the country with no pavement in sight for hours.

Week by week during spring of 1967, Bob saw the reassignment orders for soldiers arriving or departing the base, including the wounded Vietnam returnees arriving at the hospital. A pattern emerged. Over a four-month period in early 1967, four out of five departing soldiers went to Vietnam while the fifth went to Europe. This pattern stayed as regular as clockwork and clearly showed the odds of your assignment. Bob also learned it was almost certain that as he was a soldier with twenty months left to serve, he would be sent overseas. Only if you had less than one year to serve were your chances of overseas assignment low.

Bob and his friends hoped for the best but wanted to prepare for the worst. Best to enjoy Fort Gordon and Augusta while they could.

By May 1, Bob had completed the hospital "utilization and requirements" study, which required him to visit all the wards. He had the opportunity to meet some real heroes who had recently returned from Vietnam. Most of the wounded were from the First Air Cavalry Division, the First Infantry Division, and the 173rd Airborne Infantry Brigade, which did its airborne training at Augusta and Fort Benning, Georgia. They were in good spirits for the most part and felt good about having served. Their families were visiting frequently. The Regional Returnee Rehab Plan, which brought wounded veterans back to their local region, seemed to work.

Operation Junction City was just ending in Vietnam. It had started on February 22, 1967, with the goal of finding and destroying the headquarters of the communist uprising in South Vietnam. The campaign lasted until May. It involved almost three divisions of U.S. troops and was the largest airborne operation of the Vietnam War. It ultimately failed to find the well-organized headquarters it expected, but it inflicted significant losses on the Viet Cong, as well as captured supplies and material. Now Bob was seeing some of the returning wounded. He was humbled by meeting these soldiers, and he began to feel extra good about his own service, feeling that he was supporting the soldiers in the conflict.

The First Air Cavalry Division is one of the most decorated combined arms combat divisions of the U.S. Army. Its shoulder patch is a triangular-shaped badge with the pointed side facing down. It has a yellow background with a horse head in the upper right, and a thick, black diagonal bar sloping downward from left to right in the center. The First Air Cavalry pioneered the use of helicopters on a large scale to free up the infantry from being hampered by the jungle terrain and allow them to attack wherever and whenever. Helicopters were used as troop carriers, cargo lift ships, medivacs, and aerial rocket artillery.

The First Infantry Division (the Big Red One), is the oldest continuously serving combined arms division in the U.S. Army. Its shoulder patch is pea green, shaped like baseball's home plate facing down, with a big red number 1 in the center.

The 173rd Infantry Brigade Team (Airborne) was the first major U.S. Army ground formation deployed in Vietnam. Brigade members received more than 7,700 decorations. The shoulder patch is a vertical patch with a concave ribbon on top, the blue background of which is adorned with the word "AIRBORNE" in white lettering. The main body of the vertical patch shows a large, white, eagle-like wing on a blue background. The bottom part of the wing is holding a red sword pointed to the left.

The soldiers in these units were the bravest of the brave, and they got shot up badly. From what Bob heard, though, they gave as good as they got. Many of those from the southeast of the U.S. were treated and recuperated at the U.S. Army hospital at Fort Gordon. Although many would come to question America's involvement in Vietnam, no one could question these men's bravery in answering the call to defend America.

The survey done, Bob reported to his boss, Sergeant Wilfred Miller, and then never heard more about it. Much later, Bob heard that the hospital had added beds to a total of about 300 and was designated a Class I hospital.

Finally, at the end of the second week of May, Bob saw his own name on the reassignment orders that came down that week. Sergeant Miller gave the orders to Bob personally.

Miller called Bob into his office. With a very long face, he said, "Bob, your overseas assignment has come in." There was a long pause. Bob was crestfallen. He knew there was an 80% chance of going to Vietnam, but he had hoped for the best.

Finally, after a forever-sized pause, Sergeant Miller broke out in a big grin and handed Bob the orders. "Germany!"

Hallelujah! Waves of relief sweep across Bob's face along with a mile-wide smile. Bob went back to his desk and called Phil to tell him. That evening, he called his mom, who was also worried about Bob's next assignment.

Phil was elated. "Sounds like a celebration is called for. Let's plan a trip downtown."

"Excellent. Let's have an Arturo's evening."

Later, Bob noticed that Charles Weitz and Peter Ingrassia, who were part of the "lucky seven" who'd arrived on the bus from Fort Jackson, were also on the same orders. *We should all celebrate together,* he thought.

Bob spent the last week packing and shipping some stuff to the Bronx. His orders allowed him two weeks' leave at home before reporting to the reassignment station in Frankfurt, Germany. He spoke with the logistics group, which provided him his flight reservations for his flight from Kennedy Airport to Frankfurt.

In the evening of Tuesday, May 30, the four soldiers piled into the Cutlass and headed to Arturo's for dinner. Parking was easy as usual, and they got a table near the window where they could watch folks strolling by. However, it was a Tuesday, and the streets were quiet. The food and service were great as usual. They ordered dishes of eggplant parmigiana, chicken cacciatore, the special of the night, and a seafood stew in a red sauce. Garlic bread and a salad topped things off.

The jukebox was rocking the house too. A new Beatles song was playing. Just a couple of days before, the Beatles had released a strange new music album that was to shake up the music world, *Sgt. Pepper's Lonely Hearts Club Band.* This album would remain number one in the U.S. charts for fifteen weeks and become a craze all over Europe.

The evening was going splendidly. They could not resist toasting their good fortune, and each ordered a Yuengling lager on tap. "Mmm, delicious." There was joy and relief at the table. After a couple of toasts, the food arrived and everyone ordered another beer.

Finally, after all the good food and drink was finished, they each chipped in to pay the bill and eased out of the restaurant. The night had darkened. Phil drove back to the base, slowly as usual, but they soon had a moment of panic and despair. On Route 1, heading north, they saw flashing lights behind them in the distance.

"Oh, shit," Phil said, taking extra care to stay under the speed limit and in the center of the lane.

The lights came closer. Bob saw his life flashing before him. Would he not make it to Germany? Would he be arrested so soon after getting his own license? The anxiety was palpable in all four soldiers' faces. Finally, after the longest thirty seconds of Bob's life, the Augusta police car passed them and sped up, presumably on the way to a real problem.

"Phew!"

All four were instantly relieved of the moment's anguish. Shortly after, they arrived safely back on the base, the car mercifully parked safely, their futures still intact. They had all learned a valuable lesson. No worry before it's time.

Bob remembered a story he had read about General Ulysses S. Grant. Shortly before Lee's surrender at Appomattox Courthouse, Grant had developed a brutal, recurring migraine headache. No remedies or doctors' advice could cure it. This went on for weeks until, one moment after Lee signed the surrender document, Grant's headache suddenly vanished.

On his last day, Bob said his goodbyes to Sergeant Miller, who had treated him well, and to Phil Reeder, who would also leave Fort Gordon shortly to travel to Fort Dix, New Jersey, and be mustered out of the service. He also said goodbye to two of the lucky seven, even though they were destined to remain together. Most of his stuff shipped, Bob stowed his green duffel bag, closed with the pressure clip at the top, in the luggage compartment of the Greyhound bus and raced back to the Bronx for a two-week leave before boarding the plane for Frankfurt, Germany. On the bus ride home, Bob sat back and relaxed. He was basking in the relief that Vietnam was off the table. He felt optimistic and capable. And he now had a driver's license.

Bob wondered what he would do during the two-week leave in the Bronx. Would he go back to some of the old haunts or bad habits? He thought about Yonkers Raceway, where he had spent far too much time over the past five years.

**Yonkers Raceway**

There is an old saying: "When you don't know where you are going, any road will get you there."

And in the South Bronx, one of the roads to the wrong place led to Yonkers Raceway. Only eight miles from the neighborhood, it was a fifteen-minute car ride for the friend who had a car, and Bob and his friends started going there frequently. The camaraderie this activity provided became important to Bob. Because of his youth, he didn't find it easy to connect in his early college years.

Yonkers Raceway hosted standardbred racing, or harness racing, as it was called. The horses would race with one of two gaits, either pacing or trotting, and pull the driver along in a two-wheeled cart called a sulky. There was something mesmerizing about the motion of the sulkies and the spinning of the wheels that captured your attention. Bob truly enjoyed watching the races unfold, even without the excitement of the betting.

Thoroughbred racing, which Bob watched a couple of times, just did not have the same visual magic. The thoroughbred racetracks were far larger, and the horses less visible during the race as the thoroughbreds sped to the finish line all in a jumble. No, harness racing was a far more beautiful sight to watch. It turned out to be a bad habit, though, and a time-waster. But on this trip home from Fort Gordon, Bob chose to remember one of the nicer experiences he'd had at Yonkers.

It was a Thursday evening and Bob wanted to be by himself, so he let the other guys drive home after dropping him at the Raceway Diner, right near the racetrack on Yonkers Avenue. Bob slid into a booth and ordered a cheeseburger deluxe and coffee. Moments later, another youngish fellow entered and sat in the booth opposite. He was about the same size as Bob, with ruddy features, dark hair, and a straightforward smile.

He ordered and, while they were waiting for their food, said, "I see you are looking at the racing form. Any tips?"

"Not really. I am just reviewing the few races I saw this evening."

So, they struck up a conversation. The other fellow, Joshua Stotzletter, turned out to be a trainer and part of a harness racing family. They lived on a large farm in Intercourse, PA, raised crops, and bred and trained standardbred horses. An hour later, as they got ready to leave, Joshua invited Bob to his family's farm the following weekend, and Bob accepted. Friday came and Bob took the bus to Yonkers Raceway to meet Joshua, who drove them to Intercourse.

The farm was huge. Bob had seen nothing like it. Even the bungalow colony in the Catskills, although large, was kind of scraggly in its appearance. The Stotzletter farm was large and very well maintained. It had a manicured lawn in front of a big Dutch-style house, and there was a huge but perfectly maintained corral nearby. In the corral were five or six horses, wandering around and grazing.

Josh introduced Bob to some of the family and showed him to a spare room. Bob unpacked and got into bed for the night. In the morning, Josh showed Bob around the farm, the corral, the big Dutch barn, and the horse training area.

Dinner was a real family affair. There were thirteen family members around the table, and the meal progressed with lots of talking about the day's activities. A couple of the children were about to start college. The food was served family style with different meats and farm-grown vegetables followed by a wonderful rhubarb pie and coffee for dessert. Bob chatted with Joshua for a while longer, then turned in for the night.

That Sunday was a truly amazing day for Bob. Breakfast with the whole family was the same as dinner, except not everyone was there. Some had gone out to work already. A long, buffet-style table was covered with food – bacon and eggs, some kind of porridge, bread and muffins of every sort, and juice and coffee. Bob saw a vision of a lifestyle that many would aspire to. After freshening up, Joshua was going to head to the meeting hall for the Sunday morning gathering. He asked Bob to accompany him. Bob agreed, and they headed to the barn and hitched a single horse to a black, two-person, enclosed carriage that was open in the front.

"Bob, why don't you drive?" Joshua suggested.

Bob was taken aback, but he broke out in a big grin and took the reins. For the next twenty minutes, Bob had his only experience ever driving a horse-drawn cart. He drove it three miles down a road outside the Pennsylvania Dutch town of Intercourse. For twenty minutes, Bob was a harness driver, and he relished every minute of it.

He also saw the difficulties. It reminded him of being out of control driving the stick shift BMW. He also realized that one of the most important qualities of a harness driver was arm strength as they needed to rein in the powerful creatures from time to time. That unforgettable experience helped form Bob's image of the type of life one could aspire to.

With that pleasant memory in his mind, Bob nodded off to sleep on the bus. He was awakened as they approached New York and the bus's destination at the New York Port Authority Bus Terminal on 40th Street and Eighth Avenue in Manhattan.

The two-week leave passed uneventfully. Most of Bob's friends were either busy or had moved away, but Bob preferred to hang out alone for those two weeks anyway. He didn't want to do anything crazy and risk missing his flight to Germany. He knew that if all stayed well, he would be sitting at JFK Airport, waiting for a flight to Frankfurt, in two weeks.

Sarah made her famous pot roast, and Bob ate well. He took long walks, to the Yankee Stadium and the nearby parks, and reminisced about his past. He took the IRT #4 train from 167th Street and Jerome Avenue to Grand Central Station. He walked up to Rockefeller Center and went into the Warwick Hotel lobby, not knowing when he would see those places again. He knew he would be leaving everything behind, including some old friends and definitely some bad habits. He did not go to the scenes of those bad habits, consciously relegating them to the past.

Bob stayed firm. His exit from the Bronx was well underway, and he wondered what would happen on the next leg of his journey.

# Chapter Three – Heidelberg, July '67

**Arrival in Heidelberg**

His two-week leave up, Bob reported to Fort Dix, New Jersey, per his orders. Within a week, he was sitting on an airliner at JFK Airport, waiting for takeoff. At about 8 pm, the jumbo-sized charter plane screeched down the runway and slowly lifted off. Bob listened to the wheels retract as the giant silver plane slowly climbed to about 30,000 feet for the almost straight shot from JFK to Frankfurt, Germany, traveling northeast across the Atlantic.

Bob's first trip outside the United States was a leap into the unknown. He was happy he had studied French and Spanish in school, but he was flying to Germany. Further, being Jewish, he was uncertain how he would feel living there and how he would interact with the people he met.

From his window seat, Bob watched his neighbor in the center seat prepare for the journey. They would arrive in the morning and begin a day that might be long and tedious. His neighbor quickly ate the food he had brought along, then headed for the bathroom with his toothbrush.

When he returned, he saw the look Bob gave him and said, "You know it's six hours later right now in Germany. That is 2 am. So, if you're smart, you'll try to get some sleep."

Bob decided to listen to his neighbor. He had bought a sandwich at one of the kiosks, so he wolfed it down, then rushed to the bathroom, brushed his teeth, and returned to his seat. Bob's neighbor already had his shoes off, his seat reclined, and a sleeping mask over his face. Bob knew he was in the presence of a master and followed suit. Not having a sleeping mask, he got out the extra t-shirt from his carry-on bag, placed it over his face, and reclined the seat, hoping to get some sleep and be ready for whatever happened the next day in Germany.

Unable to drift off to sleep immediately, Bob thought about the Bronx. He thought about one summer at the bungalow in the Catskills in New York. It was one of his earliest memories and one of his fondest. It was early morning, and quiet. Only the birds were talking and singing. Uncle Morris collected him and took him berry picking. They walked along a little-used path nearby, each carrying a silvery, galvanized zinc pail with a circular handle. They walked around for an hour, going into the bushes as needed to pick the beautiful, black huckleberries and toss them into the pail. After an hour, the pails were each half full, and they began the walk back along the path to the bungalows. Washed in tap water, the huckleberries were sprinkled on top of a bowl of Cheerios for a fantastic breakfast. Nothing on the pavements of the Bronx could beat that. Replaying these images relaxed Bob to the point of sleep. Much later, he would rely on this memory to lower his blood pressure before he needed medication to do that.

Finally in a very relaxed state in his window seat on the plane, Bob drifted off to sleep. In the morning, the arrival at Frankfurt went smoothly. Frankfurt Airport was located on the southwest edge of town. Rhein-Main U.S. Air Base, the largest airbase in Europe, was located in the southern part of the airport.

With only 66 pounds of gear allowed on the flight, Bob carried his distinctive green duffel bag with his military number stenciled in white to the ground transportation area. The rest of his things had been shipped to a depot in Frankfurt. He would collect them later.

At the ground transportation area, he boarded a U.S. Army bus waiting to take him into Frankfurt. His stop was a place called the Gibbs Kaserne. A Kaserne is essentially a barracks, or in this case, a large brick-faced building compound with administrative offices and dormitory rooms. The reassignment station at Gibbs Kaserne processed almost all U.S. troops arriving in Germany. In mid-1967, about five hundred U.S. soldiers were redeployed throughout Germany each week from there.

It was a Monday in mid-June. It was a sunny, beautiful day with only a few puffy white clouds in the sky. Bob was shown into a great hall, where he grabbed a seat. Already, about 400 of the 500 or so seats in the large auditorium had been taken, and the rest were quickly filling up with GIs in their dress green uniforms. The auditorium was a sea of green. 500 duffel bags were left in the back. No problem to find your own later thanks to your military number stenciled in white. Bob was glad he had gotten some sleep. *This will be one long day,* he thought.

Finally, a half-hour later, a sergeant stepped onto the stage and addressed the crowd. "You are here to be reassigned to a post in Germany. For some of you, it will happen today. The final ones will take all of this week. So relax and wait and all will be well. By the weekend, you will be in your new post."

Nothing else for another half-hour. Bob and his neighbors chatted about where they were from and where they hoped to go. The fellow on his right was from upper New York State. "I want to go to Munich. I hear it's a great town. Good restaurants, sports, and Hofbräu beer on tap," he said.

What happened next was the real surprise. The sergeant returned and called out five names, asking those soldiers to come up front with their bags.

Bob was one of them. *Oh-oh, not good,* he thought.

He had heard some old sayings about the army along the way. "Never volunteer; don't get singled out; hurry up and wait." So being singled out so soon did not seem to bode well.

The sergeant led the lucky five to a suite of rooms off the auditorium and had them sit.

"A review of your orders shows that you all have the military occupational specialty of personnel specialist and about five or six months in the job. Because you understand how to read and create orders, we need your help to process these five hundred soldiers this week," he said. "This is a very important task. If you do this successfully, we will work with you to get you the best assignments available when we reassign you at the end of the week."

Later, Bob learned that the importance of this mission was to free up the sergeants for their own more important mission on the local golf course. They all happily agreed, hoping it would lead to good assignments at the end of the week.

After an hour's training, they were installed in offices and ready to go. About 100 soldiers per day were moved out to Kaiserslautern, Frankfurt, Mannheim, Munich, Stuttgart, and a variety of other posts. The work went quickly, and Bob felt he was helping the army by becoming a useful gear in the great military machine.

By the end of the week, only the fabulous five were left. The sergeant was pleased and let them know it. "Congratulations! You guys have done a great job. So now, where do you want to go?"

The choices were somewhat slimmer by then, though.

The sergeant explained that there was one job opening right there at the reassignment station. The benefits included long stretches of doing nothing, on a schedule of twelve or fourteen hours per day for three or four days per week, depending on the needs of the reassignment station.

So, you would have plenty of time to spend in Frankfurt or to take short trips nearby. This schedule did not appeal to Bob, who wanted something more regular. Interestingly, the soldier who took that job was the only one who was reassigned, only two months later, to Vietnam. Bob got lucky again.

Bob requested Munich, but there were no openings. The sergeant suggested Heidelberg, saying it was "good duty." So started a sixteen-month love affair with a small college town on the Neckar River about fifty miles south of Frankfurt.

To arrange this assignment, the sergeant telephoned Heidelberg. A fellow named Frank Cassiere answered and interviewed Bob for the position. Cassiere asked several questions about education and work experience. It turned out that a college degree was required for this position. At the end, Cassiere asked, "How much do you drink?"

To some degree, everyone tailors job interview answers to what the interviewer would like to hear. However, taken aback by this question, Bob did not know the "correct" response, so he fell back on his personal default: the truth. "I drink occasionally but not too much."

Bob didn't know why, but that answer was the right one, and he was summoned to Heidelberg for a further interview. Many months later, the purpose of the drinking question became clear when Bob and Frank became roommates. They often went out eating and drinking, and as he drank less, Bob was always able to get them home safely at the end of the night.

On Saturday, the sergeant arranged for Bob to get passage on a military truck headed for Heidelberg. The big, brown, canvas-topped truck, merged onto the Autobahn in Frankfurt around noon and swiftly ate up the fifty miles to Heidelberg. Similar trucks passed them going to Frankfurt from the south. They could be identified by their brown color and the big white star on the side canvas. In Heidelberg, the truck swung off the highway on the south side of the Neckar River and traveled several miles to the barracks in the southern part of town, arriving in the early afternoon. The truck turned onto a drive-through street under the center of a long three-story red brick building marking the entrance to Campbell Barracks.

**Campbell Barracks**

Campbell Barracks was the home to the headquarters of U.S. Army Europe and Seventh Army (USAREUR/7A). It was located on the southern outskirts of Heidelberg, near the suburb of Rohrbach.

The first allied troops entered Heidelberg on March 30, 1945, a day after German army units retreated across the Neckar River and blew up the old bridge near the Schloss. The barracks was named after Staff Sergeant Charles L. Campbell, 14th Infantry Regiment, 71st Infantry Division. On March 28, 1945, two days before the surrender of Heidelberg, Campbell led a patrol across the Rhine River near Mannheim and was killed while covering the withdrawal of his patrol as it returned to the West Bank with valuable information. Campbell was awarded the Distinguished Service Cross posthumously for extraordinary heroism.

Bob thanked the driver for the ride and headed into the main administration building. Learning that Frank Cassiere was in another building across the street, Bob walked over, his green duffel bag slung over his shoulder. Frank's office was located in an open bullpen area, where he had a larger space in a corner, near a window.

Frank was taller than Bob. He was about six feet tall and medium weight with a slim, lanky kind of look. He had a full head of brown hair combed back, a light complexion, a square jaw, and a wide smile. Frank was movie-star handsome. He was friendly, and Bob appreciated that.

After chatting for an hour or so, Frank gave Bob the signal that he would like him to stay and work there. As it was Saturday and there was no need to report for work until 8 am Monday morning, Frank escorted Bob to the dormitory building, about a five-minute walk from the office. It was there that Bob learned he would be Frank's roommate. Their room was on the second floor of a nondescript red brick building. There were two bunks to a room, and the bathrooms were down the hall. The room looked cozy, but it was big enough to comfortably hold two beds and a two-by-four footlocker with room for boots underneath. The room was painted a light shade of army green and had a small coat closet to finish it off. Home sweet home.

Frank had a heart of gold, and they would spend much quality time together both in Heidelberg and traveling. Bob was thrilled to be his roommate. Not much of a ladies' man, he could see the advantages of traveling in Frank's wake. After getting Bob settled, Frank showed him around Campbell Barracks for an hour or so until dinner time.

First, they dropped by the fully stocked PX. Any food or drink (not alcohol), sundries, stationery to write home, and almost anything you could want was there. Then the bowling alleys. Then the movie theater – a big 300 seat theater showing first-run movies. There was a baseball field nearby, and plenty of diagonal parking for those with their own cars. Finally, they went to the Enlisted Men's club. There, you could meet friends, eat, drink and play cards. Best of all, there was live entertainment, with acts coming from all over the world, including America.

Wow! Campbell Barracks was the closest thing to a resort you could find in the U.S. Army.

"The commander-in-chief of all the U.S. forces in Europe is a four-star general and is here at this HQ in Heidelberg," Frank explained. "I imagine that someone in the command prefers the soldiers spend more time at their post than interacting with civilians off the base. And so, the amenities are so spectacular. You have to really want to do something outside in order to leave."

Frank also recounted some unfortunate incidents with civilians that had taken place in the past. Since Campbell

Barracks had been upgraded with all its amenities, incidents were down considerably.

By 6 pm, it was time for dinner. Frank and Bob walked over to the Enlisted Men's club and sat at a table with some of Frank's friends. Some worked in the same office, and Frank introduced Bob to everyone. Dinner consisted of a double cheeseburger, fries, and a salad. All washed down with a Heidelberg beer on tap. Heidelberg Schloss was the brand, named after the famous castle that sat on the hill on the south side of the Neckar River. In Germany, Bob learned later, almost every town had its own brewery, although the royalty of beer remained the Munich-based brands like Hofbräu.

The Enlisted Men's club was a large cavernous space. Just past the entrance was a long wooden bar with mirrors behind and hundreds of liquor and wine bottles on the shelf below the mirrors. Past the bar was a large area with seating for about three hundred or so. The walls were finished with a brown wood veneer, and TVs were mounted on the walls in various places. The many long, rectangular tables could seat eight and had white, shiny, Formica tops.

To one side of the center of the room, there was a magnificent stage, set about two feet off the floor with several spots built out so the performers could be closer to the audience. A sound-absorbing ceiling, great lighting, and a large dance floor between the stage and the tables completed what was one of the most professional clubs in the U.S. Army. Bob and his friends would spend many evenings there over the next fifteen months.

At 7 pm, a live band came on stage. That night, it was a German group of five men and a couple of female dancers in miniskirts. The group was known as Fats and His Cats. In this first glimpse of his new life, Bob saw immediately how the Germans were crazy about jazz and soul music.

Fats was a big bear of a man with a round, chubby, goateed face that always had a smile. Brown hair combed straight back and black, oversized "Roy Orbison" glasses completed his look. He sang and played the guitar and various reed instruments. The Cats were all dressed in dark pants and dinner jackets. Fats' jacket was a different color, a maroon red.

Fats and His Cats played a set for about an hour, including "Mustang Sally," an incredibly popular song released by Wilson Pickett the year before. Later, in the fall, Fats started singing a new song that had just been released, "Soul Man," by Sam and Dave. This song was to be Fats' signature song for the next year or so. Fats and the group personified that soul sound and had the audience rocking and dancing. It permeated the room with an electricity like an oncoming thunderstorm.

Bob knew right away he should not have limited himself to taking judo lessons. He should have kept going and learned to dance. As it turned out, he would rectify this only after returning to the U.S. fifteen months later.

After a great evening of food and music, Bob and Frank returned to their room to turn in for the night. The food quality had been mediocre at best. It was comfort food. But then, the food was not the point. It was about the music, the ambiance, and being with friends almost any night you wanted.

Frank had plans the next day, so Bob went walking in the old town for part of the day. He had a bratwurst, sauerkraut, and a delicious German beer on tap at a local café. In the afternoon, he returned to the barracks and stopped by the PX to buy some shaving cream, razor blades, brass polish, shoe polish, and a couple of sodas before going to his room. He wanted to get some rest and be bright-eyed to start his new job the next morning.

Frank was still out with friends, so Bob relaxed on his bunk. Having seen the Enlisted Men's club and the downtown café, he knew one thing for sure. He was not going to have enough money to take advantage of everything available in Heidelberg. He realized this even before learning about all the travel opportunities that would come his way. Heidelberg was incredibly well located in Western Europe for those who wanted to travel. Bob knew he would have to somehow acquire the funds to make the most of his new life. As he relaxed on his bunk, he thought back to his first year of college and his first attempts to make some money.

**Alexander's Department Store**

It was summer and hot on the streets of the Bronx. Bob needed some money, so he decided to try the time-honored way for a Bronx teenager to earn money: work at Alexander's Department Store on Fordham Road.

Alexander's had opened its Bronx store in 1933. It had become wildly successful selling discounted clothing and other items to the Bronx residents living through the Great Depression. Located on Fordham Road at Valentine Avenue, it was a big, white block of a building, facing diagonally into the street and sporting a gigantic rooftop sign that read *Uptown, it's ALEXANDER'S.*

Bob's older cousin had given him the idea. "You should try Alexander's. I have a couple of friends who work there. It's easy work and the hours are flexible, so you could still do well in school."

Bob took a trip there to apply. After a twenty-minute bus ride on the B2 bus, he got off at Fordham Road and walked two blocks to the store. The huge, rooftop sign could be seen from blocks away. On the way to the store, he passed the RKO Fordham – a popular movie theater, a Fannie Farmer candy store, and a Benhil shoe store. Later, Bob would buy his shoes at the latter. "Nothing like a new pair of Florsheim shoes to make you feel prosperous," he would later say.

Bob got the job and was elated to receive his first real paycheck. That someone would have him officially on the payroll, with taxes taken out too, made Bob feel that he was on his way. Unfortunately, the feeling wore off quickly. At $4.00 per hour, four hours per day, three days per week, he was netting about $36 per week after taxes. Each workday, Bob wolfed down a sandwich his mom prepared for him and walked to the Grand Concourse to catch the bus to Fordham Road. He walked the last two blocks and entered the huge store through a side entrance. He walked down a narrow, nondescript corridor with bright overhead lighting and a beige linoleum floor to the time clock on the wall near the door to the main store. He picked out his time card from the section of S's and punched in. He repeated the process in reverse on the way out.

Working in the men's clothing department, Bob became knowledgeable about fabrics. 100% cotton shirts in the summer felt cooler in the heat, and the magical dacron polyester that refused to wrinkle became his favorites.

After about six months, the job had turned into a grind. But the real problem was that $36 per week went only so far. Between bus fare, food and drinks, and an occasional pair of shoes at Benhil, he was spending the money as fast as he got it, sometimes faster. So after about six months, with the arrival of winter in the South Bronx, Bob decided that he would not make his fortune there and quit. He would devote his energies to school and stay poor for the time being.

Although Bob had saved none of his earnings, he kept the fond memories of Alexander's, Benhil Shoes, and stopping in at Krum's once in a while for an ice cream soda.

His education about clothing and fabrics would also stay with him. Much later, he became particular about what he wore.

Bob was brought back from his memories of Alexander's by Frank returning to their room. They chatted, then got ready for dinner.

"I'll meet you at the Enlisted Men's club. I want to call home first," Bob said.

He stopped by the PX and called home and spoke with his mom. She was still working at Ohrbach's on 34th Street. Bob was glad to hear that she was in good health. Henry was well too; he had just changed jobs and become a supervisor of computer operations at a new computer service bureau in lower Manhattan. He was living in Queens and thinking of marrying his girlfriend Anna, who also worked at the service bureau. Uncle Warner was still getting up at 2 am to buy fresh fish at the Fulton Street market, and all seemed right in the world.

Sarah, a widow for seven years now, was thinking of moving to a new development in the northeast Bronx called Co-Op City. Construction was underway on the site formerly known as Freedomland. It promised more spacious apartments and a safer environment than her present neighborhood, which unfortunately was undergoing dramatic change. Sarah's eventual move to Co-Op City happened much later. Unfortunately for Bob, he was in California at the time. Somehow, Bob's baseball autograph collection was misplaced during the move and never found again. At least the memories remained.

Bob told Sarah about his money problem. "This is the opportunity of a lifetime for me, mom. From Heidelberg, I can travel anywhere in Europe. Who knows if I'll get the chance again?" He explained that his army pay was not enough to travel, and he was willing to go into debt if Sarah could lend him the money.

"You know things are still tight for me and I need to be ready to pay some money down to move into Co-Op City when that happens," his mom said.

"I understand," he said, "but I need this money and I will let nothing prevent me from paying you back on time."

Sarah made no promises but told Bob she would see what she could do.

The Heidelberg assignment became a pivotal point in Bob's military career, and in his life. One of the many things the town would provide was a model of how great life could be in a small college town in a rural environment. Heidelberg had just the right amount of pavement, a countryside that always beckoned, and a great institution of learning in the background. Bob was incredibly excited and optimistic about the next fifteen months. Many years later, a similar small college town by the name of Princeton, New Jersey, would beckon, and Bob would jump at the chance to live there with his wife and son.

**The Office**

Bob's excitement carried over to Monday morning. He arrived at the office at 8 am sharp, in a fresh green dress uniform, brass lapel pins, and black shoes shined to a high polish. He stopped to see Frank, who introduced him to Staff Sergeant George Hansen from Colorado, his new boss. George Hansen was "Regular Army," meaning he had enlisted for three years. He had been lucky enough to draw the Heidelberg assignment and was finishing his enlistment there, in charge of part of the office. Hansen welcomed Bob, showed him to his desk, and gave him a brief overview of the operation.

It was very special. HQ USAREUR and Seventh Army were responsible for about 230,000 U.S. soldiers throughout Germany. The HQ was divided into two Adjutant General units, located in two separate buildings on the campus. One unit was responsible for all personnel in the U.S. Army in Germany. The other unit, Bob's, was responsible for all the soldiers at the USAREUR headquarters, about 2,000 to 3,000 personnel in all.

This elite office was composed of 20 to 25 people, including four civilian administrative assistants and now Bob. Hansen reported to a captain, who reported to a full bird colonel, who reported to a four-star general. That was how it was.

To get into this fraternity, you needed a college degree and good scores on the battery of intelligence tests taken right after induction. Frank had vetted Bob, but now he was his colleague and roommate. George Hansen was their boss.

The rest of this elite group were from all parts of the country: Chicago, Los Angeles, San Francisco, Denver, Cleveland, Milwaukee, Richmond, Boston, New York, and a scattering of other places. They were all about the same age and the majority had been drafted, although some had enlisted for three years.

All the single fellows lived in the barracks on base. However, any married soldier who brought their spouse could live off-base, and four or five of the men had taken the off-base option. Although he didn't know it then, Bob would soon realize the great benefits of off-base housing.

Bob settled into the office routine and quickly learned the nuts and bolts of personnel administration in the U.S. Army. It was amazing how many ordinary things had to be done to keep the military machine in motion. Leaves, three-day passes, promotions, and transfers just scratched the surface.

Bob also became an expert in Line of Duty investigations, investigating and reporting on the steady stream of incidents that occurred all over Germany. Some were completed quickly, others lingered. On the day that Bob arrived, a soldier was killed in an auto accident. The various legal, family, and army investigations and reports were still not completed fifteen months later when Bob returned to the U.S. Other investigations were completed quickly.

Within a month, Bob knew almost everything he needed to know. He had become part of a very close-knit group at the office, an elite fraternity of young college graduates making the military machine in Europe work.

Most of those at the office were off work by noon on Fridays because almost everyone had a second military job. After three weeks, Bob's name reached the sergeant major of the Seventh Army, also located at Campbell Barracks. Bob got a phone call from Sergeant Major John Tucker asking him to come over as Bob had been assigned to him. The Seventh Army was one of the most strategic military units in Europe. At that time, it was the Armored Division (Tank Corps) and the main bulwark protecting Western Europe from a potential Russian invasion of the West. The group would continue to be of major importance throughout the cold war.

Unlike Bob's unit, the Seventh Army was a combat unit, and as such, would go on maneuvers once or twice a year to practice making war. Just like General Patton had said, this was the primary purpose of a soldier.

Bob's imagination ran wild as he headed over to see the sergeant major that afternoon. Sergeant Major Tucker was about five feet six inches tall, with a stocky, muscular build, short sandy hair, and a deep gravelly voice. When he spoke, you could see all of his immaculate white teeth bulging out of his mouth. His face was weathered. He had seen a few things.

They chatted for fifteen minutes or so while he took Bob's measure. He explained that Bob worked for the Seventh Army on Saturday mornings and he was to report each Saturday morning to him.

"I also expect you to drive my Jeep when I have to travel on weekends and when we are on maneuvers," he added.

Bob hesitated for a moment, then said, "Well that is fine, but I don't have a military driver's license and am not too good with a stick shift."

Sergeant Major Tucker looked at Bob and gathered his thoughts for a moment. "Well, that's OK. You don't need a license to clean the Jeep. So be here every Saturday morning and clean it well. I want it to shine."

"No problem," said Bob. "I can do that."

Sergeant Major Tucker smiled, showing his immaculate white teeth, and let Bob leave. He saw they understood one another. Much later, Bob would go on a secret mission for the sergeant major during one of those two-week maneuvers.

By the end of July, Bob had settled in. He knew his job, he admired [illegible] spected his group of colleagues, and he [illegible] o go out eating and drinking, as long as [illegible] ıt. He had become a member of a [illegible] that had eluded him in college.

[illegible] noon about a month after Bob had [illegible] finished hosing down the Jeep and making it shine. He had about four hours before heading over to the Enlisted Men's club for dinner.

Wanting to resume his exercise program, he decided to go for a run. The big park-like space behind the barracks had a baseball field, but also a running track. Bob walked the five minutes to the barracks, changed into a lightweight polo shirt and gym-type shorts. On the track, he began to warm up with some stretching. He had not run since he'd arrived in Germany and was in no rush. He had four hours to dinner, and fifteen months before heading home. He knew that it would be the easiest thing in the world to get totally out of shape in Heidelberg. He refused to allow that to happen. Over the years, he had invested a lot in his physical fitness, and he would do whatever it took to maintain what he had gained.

The track was deserted. Only a few GIs were there, tossing a baseball around on the ball field. While warming up, Bob let his mind drift back to the Bronx.

**Running at the Park Near the Yankee Stadium**

Bob first started to exercise when he was about fourteen. His life was centered on two places – Fordham Road, two miles north, and the Yankee Stadium, about half a mile south. Near the Yankee Stadium was Mullaly Park, which had a running track. Bob had no idea about how to run back then, but he gave it a try. It was his introduction to exercise, soon to be followed by judo, then weightlift[illegible] He ran on that track several afternoons a week[illegible] slow at first but began to increase his speed [illegible] after a few months. These improvements were a great source of satisfaction.

At fifteen, Bob had been running for a year. One afternoon, as he finished his fourth lap around the quarter-mile track at Mullaly Park in the Bronx, a fellow he did not recognize came onto the track and switched into his running clothes. He was in no rush to start but warmed up thoroughly with a variety of stretching exercises. He was a little taller than Bob and a lot more muscular. His calves were bulging as he warmed up. He had a ruddy complexion and wavy, flaming red hair. Finally, the stranger began to run in the same direction as Bob.

Bob picked up his pace, proud of his improved running ability. Quickly, he realized this fellow was no ordinary runner. By the time he was halfway around the next lap, the stranger had come around a full lap and bypassed Bob. Over the next forty minutes, the red-headed stranger ran two laps for every one of Bob's, putting Bob's running improvements into true perspective.

Bob had no chance to speak to the stranger that day, but he consulted a friend who was a top-flight runner and ran in the Boston Marathon each year, always finishing about 250th, a very respectable result. Bob described the redhead to Allen and asked, "Do you know the guy? I've never seen anyone run like that."

"Of course," Allen said. "That's MacDonald! He finishes around 50th in the Boston Marathon every year."

Bob ran with MacDonald many times after that and always gave him the credit for the inspiration to improve. Not that they ran together, as Bob could never keep up. They just ran in each other's presence.

**Running in Heidelberg**

Now, fully warmed up and back from his memories of Mullaly Park, Bob got out on the track behind the barracks in Heidelberg on that beautiful sunny day in July and channeled his inner MacDonald. He slowly lapped the track eight times to make two miles. He felt great afterward, sweating hard and breathing heavily. He completed the workout with about a hundred pushups and headed for a shower before dinner. He had resumed his exercise program, determined to return home in great physical shape, despite the nice life ahead in Heidelberg.

The next week, Richard Jones, one of the fellows at the office, suggested they go to the local swimming pool in Heidelberg. Rich was a little taller than Bob with a lean build and close-cropped sandy brown hair parted on one side. A pair of black glasses completed his look, and his infectious smile made him popular with everyone. He was a straight shooter from Cleveland, Ohio, and you could trust him with anything.

"Since you are back to exercising," Rich said, "why don't we head over to the Schwimmbad Saturday afternoon, after your Jeep duty? I'll drive." Rich had an old Ford that he'd bought in Heidelberg.

Bob was happy to go. "Great," he said. "I'm in. I get off at 1 pm, so I can be ready by 1:30."

On Saturday afternoon, they left Campbell Barracks and drove the three miles to the Schwimmbad in Rohrbach. The German people loved to exercise. You could see bicycles everywhere, and almost every community had a public, outdoor swimming pool. The facility in Rohrbach had an Olympic-size pool surrounded by a concrete walkway. On one end of the huge rectangular pool, there was a smaller square pool with two diving platforms: a high platform and a low platform. Near the pools, there was a lawn area for sunbathing, a café, and some playground equipment for children. Families could stay for hours.

Bob was used to swimming at Orchard Beach in the Bronx, but he had not seen anything like this. He watched in amazement as the adults and many children climbed up the steep ladder to the high platform and dove off. Bob loved being there, and they would visit the Schwimmbad almost every weekend in the summer. However, he never had the nerve to dive off either diving platform. Those who did, he considered heroes. Much later, Bob would windsurf six miles across a windswept bay in Long Island and six miles back, but diving from such a height remained beyond his limits.

That evening, Bob and Rich met four others from the office for dinner at the Enlisted Men's club. A new band from Spain called the Zaras was performing. They played all the popular dance songs of the day and rocked the house. They became an instant hit and performed many times after that. They sang a song that was flying on the charts, "Give Me Some Lovin'" by the Spencer Davis Group. This became their signature song. Their music range was wide, including rock, pop, soul, and disco. *Sgt. Pepper's Lonely Hearts Club Band* was already a huge hit, so they sang many Beatles songs too. Many years later, Bob would drive to Hartford Connecticut from New York to see them perform on their America tour.

The food was the usual comfort food of burgers and fries, and the Schloss Beer on tap was great. That night, Bob learned a drinking game called Pass the Boot, which required five or six players. A two-liter glass beer stein in the shape of a boot is passed around the table clockwise. Each person in turn drinks whatever amount they wish. But when the boot is finally emptied, the drinker before the finisher must pay for the next boot. A devilish game invented in the beer halls, but so enjoyable.

By 10 pm, the Zaras' second set was over and some heads were beginning to droop. Bob looked over at Frank's sagging head and decided to start earning his keep. He went behind Frank and leaned near his ear. "Hey Frank, I'm kind of tired and going back to the room. Why don't you join me?"

Frank gave Bob a look of disapproval, but changed his mind a minute later and joined him. Although Frank was a little wobbly, they made it back safely and slept soundly all night.

Earlier in the evening, Rich had spoken to Bob. "You know, you haven't gotten around much these last few weeks," he said. "Since you like the Schwimmbad so much, you really should buy your own car. It's easy to do and I'll show you where to find the advertisements."

"That's a great idea. Tomorrow is Sunday. Can we start then?" Bob said.

"Sure," said Rich. "It's easy to get a driver's license too. Our office processes them. Also, you could buy an older car for little money, then sell it again just before you head home."

**The Pea-Green Beetle**

Within two weeks, Bob became the proud owner of a 1956 Volkswagen Beetle. Bob was thankful for all those death-defying drives in the South Bronx in the stick shift BMW. He bought the Bug from the original owner, an elderly German in town, for $200. There was another Volkswagen for sale, owned by a soldier who was returning home, but the pea-green 1956 was in better shape. It had a little dent in one of the rear fenders, a tiny rear oval window, and running boards. It had a four-speed manual transmission, and you had to double-clutch to move into the next gear. Bob was ecstatic. For only $200, he was now mobile. If the car remained in good shape, he could sell it before his departure to the States for the same amount.

And so, after four weeks in Heidelberg, Bob was mobile and now had two vehicles to clean each Saturday.

After driving the Beetle locally for a week, Bob took a trip he knew had to be done but was dreading. For his first out-of-town trip, he had to drive to Frankfurt to pick up the baggage he had sent from home to the U.S. Army depot there.

On a Friday afternoon, Bob drove up to Frankfurt, carrying the address of the depot in his pocket. Confident in the Beetle now, he exited the barracks, got onto Bergheimer Strasse, drove three miles, and merged onto the Autobahn heading north for the fifty-minute trip to Frankfurt.

The fun only began there, though. After getting off the Autobahn in the southeast part of town, Bob soon despaired of ever finding the depot. Frankfurt was a huge town with millions of vehicles, including trucks, taxis, and a variety of other commercial vehicles. Frankfurt was also a traffic circle town. Many major intersections were circles and after five minutes of going in circles, Bob realized he was totally lost. He didn't speak the language and had no idea how to get where he was going.

Finally, in desperation, he had a brilliant idea. Right near a major circle, he pulled into a parking spot near a taxi stand. He walked ten feet or so to the nearest taxi and said hello to the driver, who was smoking a cigarette near his taxi. Bob handed the paper with the depot's address to the taxi driver. He pointed first to himself, and then to the address. The taxi driver understood. What a relief.

The driver got into his cab and started the engine. At the same time, Bob walked back to his car and got inside. But then, the taxi driver turned off his engine and walked back to Bob. He looked questioningly at Bob, as if to say "What is going on? I thought you wanted me to take you to this address."

Finally, after a two-minute game of charades, the driver understood that Bob wanted to follow the taxi in his own car. Wunderbar! Then, with perfect understanding between the two, the taxi driver led Bob and the Beetle on the eight-minute journey to the U.S. Army depot in southwest Frankfurt.

Picking up his package of clothes was easy. Bob entered the depot and handed the shipping receipt to a sergeant sitting in the anteroom. Within ten minutes, Bob had his clothes in the trunk of the pea-green Beetle outside. Interestingly, the trunk was in the front of the Beetle and the engine in the back. This configuration would save Bob much grief later.

The depot was located near the highway, and thanks to the sergeant's good directions, Bob was on the Autobahn heading back south to Heidelberg in a minute or two. Bob knew there was no speed limit on this section of the Autobahn but did not really know what that meant.

**Chaos in the Left Lane**

The trip back began uneventfully. There were many trucks on the road traveling in the right lane. Bob got behind an eighteen-wheeler with a beige canvas top and followed it for a while. Deciding to pass, he checked his driver's side mirror, saw nothing coming, and pushed the Beetle to about 70 mph, easing into the left lane.

HONK, HONK, HONK! In an instant, a big Mercedes was right on his tail, coming out of nowhere. The Mercedes driver flashed his lights and honked his horn. Bob was rattled. The next thirty seconds felt like an hour. With the Mercedes right behind, horn honking, Bob floored the gas pedal, wondering how much it could take. The ancient Beetle slowly responded, speeding up to 75 mph. After an eternity, Bob passed the truck and eased back into the right lane. The Mercedes flew by, sped up to probably 90 or 100 mph, and quickly disappeared from view. Phew! Bob exhaled, trying to recover from his near-death experience. For the rest of the trip, he dawdled in the right lane, trying to calm down.

From time to time, a car would suddenly appear in the driver's side mirror, flash by in an instant, and be gone just as quickly. Ninety minutes later, Bob was back at Campbell Barracks, the pea-green Beetle safely parked by the ball field, and the shipped clothing stored in his room. Bob breathed a sigh of relief, happy to have survived his lesson in driving on the Autobahn.

That trip was the first of many road adventures for Bob and the pea-green Beetle. Bob relaxed on his bed and thought about life. *It has been an amazing July,* he thought, wondering what August would bring.

# Chapter Four – August and September '67

They arrived and were seated at the bar. The building looked like a Swiss chalet and was located right near the bank of the Neckar River. It had an opulent ambiance. The bar room was paneled with rich mahogany wood, and there were local photographs on the walls. Located adjacent to the dining room, the bar had a cozy atmosphere and was visible from the dining room tables. They sat at three tables at the corner of the bar, ordered drinks, and waited for their table to be ready.

"Thank you all for your hard work during the inspection. I'm buying the first round," George Hansen said.

The last week of July had brought a yearly inspection of the office records by the inspector general. The full bird colonel in charge of the group had made it clear this inspection had to go well. Bob and his colleagues knew their many privileges depended on it. Were the files in order? Proper procedures followed? Timely notifications sent to higher command, mostly in Washington D.C.?

It was a week of long evenings at work, no partying, and little time out and about. By the end of the week, the group was exhausted but the inspection was over. Although the results were not yet known, the office breathed a collective sigh of relief. George Hansen, Bob's boss, suggested his group all go out to dinner at a local inn that they had been to before. On Friday night, ten of them went out to the Inn at Neckargemünd, located in a tiny rural town of the same name just three miles from Heidelberg on the south bank of the Neckar River.

Hansen was a musician and playwright by profession. He did not talk much about what had made him join the army, but he was clearly enjoying his "short-timer" status. Being a short-timer meant you would be leaving the service within ninety days or so. Generally, short-timers tried to be a little more careful so there were no delays in their departure. But Hansen actually loosened up, became friendlier and more sociable, and even did a bit of traveling. He liked the Swiss Alps, which probably reminded him of his beloved Colorado mountains.

Hansen was about six feet tall and had a solid build with a little paunch starting to show. He had a ruddy complexion and dark brown wavy hair. A great salesman, he could convince people to do what he wanted, which was the reason he was in charge of a big part of the office despite not being an officer. He mostly kept to himself and wasn't a regular at the Enlisted Men's club.

Hansen made the first toast. "Great work on the inspection. I'm sure the results will be solid."

Everyone knew that he would be back in Colorado in about eighty days, with his writing and the mountains he loved.

Sam and Cindy Kowalski were from Chicago. Sam had been drafted and had about fifteen months remaining in the service. His wife had joined him two months earlier, and they lived three miles from the base, in a nondescript two-bedroom apartment facing a garden in the back. Sam was of medium height, stocky with straight black hair, and Cindy was a petite blonde with hair the color of straw and easy to get along with.

Jack and Becky Custis were from Richmond, Virginia. Same story. He had about fifteen months remaining, and they also lived off the base. Jack was of medium height and slender. He had a homespun quality and a wry open smile. Everyone liked him. His wife, about the same height, was slender with dark brown hair and a great smile. She was very outspoken and quick with a joke. They were living the same suburban lives they had before, only now in Heidelberg.

Also at dinner were Frank Cassiere, Richard Jones, Charlie Walsh, and Arnie Bloomberg. Chuck was from Boston and slim with an athletic build. He had red hair, and his face had a few freckles here and there. He enjoyed his life, and he lit up the room when he smiled.

Arnie was from Dallas, Texas. He was of medium height, had a solid build, a square-jawed head with black hair, and black glasses. He was smart as a whip and had a wry sense of humor that closely matched Bob's. They got along great together and shared hotel rooms during their later travels.

"It's a good thing we are traveling in separate cars," Arnie said. "If we were all in an accident, U.S. Army Europe would cease functioning."

Before long, the group was seated. Two tables had been pulled together and covered with a blue and white checkered tablecloth. Bob was in the mood for steak and shared a Porterhouse steak with Arnie. It was falling off the plate and way too big for one. Shoestring fries and a big salad came with it. The beer was local, on tap, and tasted great. Their waiter, the owner's son, knew Hansen and was very attentive. The inn was known for its steaks, and most people ordered them.

"Now that the inspection is over, we should go back to the house parties," Sam said. "Cindy and I will host the next one. How about next Saturday night?"

Everyone agreed, and the date was set.

"We should also make plans to go to the Burning of the Castle. That is the following Saturday night," Becky said.

Sam did not want to go at first because he knew it meant picnicking, but he later relented and they all decided to go. Finally, when all the good food and drink was finished, they paid the bill and left, piled into the three cars, and headed back to the base.

The next week went by in a flash. Everyone was relieved with the inspection behind them, and the passing results came in on Thursday. The full bird colonel said he was pleased, and everyone cheered. Their privileges were intact and the good life in Heidelberg rolled on.

Friday came. Bob and a few others, off at noon, parked Rich's car in a parking lot near the castle and strolled downtown to see the sights. They went to the old bridge and took some photos. It was a beautiful August day, just a few long white streaks of cloud but very sunny, and warm. The town was crowded with tourists. There were two main types of tourists: Japanese businessmen taking photos of everything with expensive cameras and Australian nurses. Bob did not know why, but there were always a lot of tourists from Japan and Australia. Tourism would dry up in the winter, but it was exciting during the summer. The downtown streets swarmed with people and the cafés were crowded. They were in a place where everyone else wanted to be.

They crossed the old bridge to see the beautiful sights from the river. They saw the castle and the roads in the hills, which were all covered in greenery. They saw the beautiful red clay tile rooftops all around, a truly beautiful sight. Then they crossed back to the old town side of the Neckar and strolled along the Hauptstrasse in the direction of the old town center, the Marktplatz.

The Hauptstrasse (High Street) was the major shopping street in town. There were shops and cafés of every kind, and the street was crowded. Cars were driving down the street too. It wouldn't be until two years later, in 1969, that the Hauptstrasse would become a strictly pedestrian mall. As the sidewalks were narrow, people were walking in the street as well as on the sidewalks, so the car drivers had to be very careful.

Bob, Rich, Arnie, Charlie, and Frank left the Hauptstrasse and strolled along Untere Strasse. Untere Strasse (Lower Street) ran parallel to the Hauptstrasse in the heart of the old town, not far from the university. This narrow, cobblestoned street looked like many Mediterranean old town streets and was dotted with student pubs and cafés. It was alive with foot traffic.

They stopped at the Leipzigger wine bar. The Leipzigger had been there forever. The interior was small and dimly lit, with walls of dark wood. Behind the small wooden bar were shelves with rows of wine glasses sparkling in the overhead lights. In short, it was a great dark bar for drinking in the afternoon without sunlight intruding.

At night, the street was even more crowded and alive. Down the street were several jazz clubs that hosted jazz greats from around the world. Bob and his friends would spend some time there later on, but they were nighttime events. The jazz clubs generally did not open their doors until 8 pm or so. At 2 pm on a Friday afternoon, the Leipzigger was perfect.

They squeezed together at two small wooden tables, and the waiter brought menus. Germany was well known for Moselle wines, which were slightly sweet but wonderful tasting. They ordered a lunch of bratwurst and spaetzle and a bottle of Moselle wine.

They talked about home and their lives at Heidelberg, and toasted the just-finished inspection again, relieved to keep their privileged lifestyle for the time being. Then they started talking about some of the places they wanted to visit when the weather got colder.

"I have been getting close to this girl Linda I know back home," Charlie said. "We have been writing and talking on the phone. This may be the real thing for me."

"So what do you think you'll do about it?" Frank asked.

"I'm thinking of going to Amsterdam in the fall and picking up a diamond ring," Charlie replied.

"Wow," Bob said. "You *are* serious. Well, I hear that's not all you can pick up in Amsterdam. Maybe I'll go with you."

"I have heard that too," Charlie said. Everyone laughed.

"Switzerland is for me. I want to see the mountains. I have lived my whole life in Dallas, and I am tired of flat," Arnie said.

Frank and Rich agreed. "Count us in on a Switzerland trip," Frank said.

"I have got to go to Paris. I studied French for two years in college and I am crazy to try it out," Bob said.

"Well," Arnie said. "That is easy. Just a short train ride to Frankfurt, then switch trains for the overnight to Paris and you are there at 7 am. I would go along."

With the food finished, it was time for a second bottle of Moselle.

The place started to fill up, and jazz started playing over the speakers.

By 6 pm, they had drunk six bottles of Moselle wine and it was time to head back. Rich was the designated driver that day and had drunk little. After a ten-minute walk to shake out the cobwebs, they were back at the parking lot, and then to the barracks. Enough time to shower and head to the Enlisted Men's club for dinner and some bridge.

This time, it was Frank's turn to get Bob safely back to the room. Bob had never drunk so much wine before. Back at the room, Bob lay on his bunk and vegged out for about an hour. The other guys had left him and headed back to the club. Bob finally joined them at about 8 pm. A nondescript German band was playing pop and rock and roll, and the dance floor was crowded. Bob ordered the usual cheeseburger and fries but skipped the alcohol. He got into the bridge game when Chuck decided to leave early.

Bridge was a wonderful pastime, and they played often at the club. You could get to the club at 3 pm on a Sunday, start a bridge game, and the next thing you knew it was 10 o'clock at night. In the meantime, you had eaten dinner, had a few beers, and watched a show.

"I know you have been short on money," Frank said to Bob. "Have you thought about getting a job as a waiter here at the club? The pay is OK and the tips are very good."

"That sounds interesting. Can you introduce me to someone?"

"I'll take care of it. They are always looking for waiters."

Finally, the band played the best song of the night – Procol Harum's "Whiter Shade of Pale." The crowd loved it. The bridge game broke up, and everyone headed back to the dorms. The next day was a Saturday, and there was the party at Cindy and Sam's place that night.

Saturday morning came and went. Bob managed to get up on time and get over to the motor pool. Nothing unusual was happening, so he hosed down the Jeep, polished it to a shine, and headed back. He jumped back into bed for an hour and relaxed in the barracks, resting for the party that night.

Later in the afternoon, Bob went to the PX and called home. He got his mom right away, and they talked for a half-hour. Nothing much had changed at home. All was well. Henry was doing well at the computer service bureau and had just been promoted to operations supervisor. He was happy, and he and Anna were planning to get married soon.

"I am not comfortable lending you a large sum of money because it looks like my move to Co-Op City may happen sooner than I thought," Sarah told Bob toward the end of the call.

Bob immediately felt let down, but Sarah continued. "But what I have done is arranged a loan for you with Aunt Yolande. She will lend you up to $5,000 if you need that much. I told her how grateful you would be and that you would repay her quickly when you return."

A wave of relief swept over Bob. His nagging headache over the lack of money immediately went away. He wanted more, but $5,000 would be enough to do at least some things.

Bob showered, picked up Arnie and Chuck, and headed for Sam and Cindy's. Around 4 pm, people started arriving. Cindy put out some appetizers and provided the beer. Some brought their own drinks. Bob had brought a bottle of Johnnie Walker Black Label, which was his go-to drink. The conversation ranged from talking about what they would do when they got back home to discussing trips in Europe.

"It's an easy trip on a three-day pass. Just take the overnight train from Heidelberg and you arrive in the morning," Chuck explained to Bob, talking about taking a trip to Amsterdam.

"Sounds the same as the trip to Paris," Bob said. "Heidelberg is at the center of a circle that makes for easy traveling on a three-day pass."

Chuck had been reading about Amsterdam and was keen to share what he'd found out. "Amsterdam is a walking town, like Heidelberg. You don't need a car. The restaurants, hotels, diamond district, and museums are all within walking distance or a short trolley ride away."

Arnie had just been to Wiesbaden to buy stereo equipment. The Canadian Air Force PX in Wiesbaden had the best prices on stereo equipment, and the U.S. Army had access. Bob would later head over there and buy a Sansui solid state receiver, a Dual turntable, and a set of small speakers, spending more money he did not have. But the opportunity to play the great music they had been hearing at the clubs in his room was too good to pass up.

Cindy set out a dinner of pizza and salad, after which the party continued. They had a good sound system, and the music helped keep the party going until 10 or 11 at night. After all the good conversation, stories, and trip planning, the couples left for their own places. Bob and the other single guys fell asleep right where they were, on the floor or on sofa cushions. They awoke Sunday morning to large cups of steaming coffee and rolls and headaches.

Sunday was a quiet day, perfect for recovering. Large amounts of Coca-Cola during the day took away the headaches, and life returned to normal by Sunday evening. It had been worth the hangovers. It was just great that ten friends sharing a unique moment in time could spend a day and night together, enjoying one another's company.

**Waiter for a Night**

On Sunday night, Frank introduced Bob to Warner Eppits, who managed the bar at the Enlisted Men's club. Despite the good news from Sarah about the $5,000 loan, Bob wanted to try to earn some more.

Warner explained the job to Bob. "It couldn't be simpler. 5 to 10 pm, three nights per week. The pay is only $2.00 per hour, but the tips are very good. Just take the orders for food and drinks from the tables and give them to the bartender and the kitchen. Then return the proper order to the proper table."

Bob agreed to start the next night. Monday night was usually slower and Warner thought it would be easier to get the experience then. At 5 pm, Bob arrived at the club and started work. Franz the bartender had been there two years. He and Bob knew each other and had spoken many times.

The work was hectic even on a slow night, but Bob was determined. Whenever he picked up drinks from Franz, they would chat for a minute. After a while, though, Franz started putting an extra beer on the tray for Bob.

"Thanks. I am enjoying this job already," Bob joked.

By 9:30 pm, Bob had drunk about six beers and was practically falling over. He held it together until 10 pm when the club closed. Then the waiters did part of the clean-up, wiping off all the tables and placing the chairs on top of the tables to make it easier for the clean-up crew in the morning. Total time elapsed: six hours; total money earned: about $40 in tips – about $7 per hour; total beers drunk: about six. Bob stumbled back to the barracks and collapsed on his bed. He got to work late the next morning and was yelled at by George Hansen. That was one of the few times Bob was late for anything, and he did not like it.

*Thank goodness Sarah came through,* he thought.

That night, he told Warner Eppits that he could not continue.

**Heidelberg University**

Now he wasn't working at the Enlisted Men's club, Bob wanted to make better use of his free time. One Friday, he decided to walk around downtown by himself and visit Heidelberg University, which he had heard so much about.

The main part of the university was located right in the center of the old town. Bob started at Heidelberger Marktplatz, which was the oldest, most important square in town. On one side was the old City Hall. Opposite that was the Holy Ghost church, a 15th-century Gothic church built with local red sandstone. Bob walked down Hauptstrasse and made a left at Grabengasse, which took him directly to Universitat Platz and Neue Universitat, one of the main schools at the heart of the university. It was a large four-story white structure with a black roof, set on one side of the square. Over the double-door entry was a bronze bust of Athena (the goddess of wisdom) and a script that read *Den Lebendigen Geist* (to the living spirit).

Heidelberg University is the oldest university in Germany, dating from 1386, the third university founded in the Holy Roman Empire. It has been co-educational since 1899. The university motto is "Semper Apertus" (always open).

Bob walked around the square, then went into the lobby of the Neue Universitat building. Its lines were as clean on the inside as on the outside. A long corridor led to various offices, and crowds of students were walking through. It was Friday afternoon, a busy time, and students were coming from and going to classes.

He left the square and continued down the Grabengasse to Plock to see the old library (Universitätsbibliothek Heidelberg). It was a beautiful, ornate Collegiate Gothic building, built with red sandstone in 1905. It is said to be the busiest library in Germany. Years later, Bob would see very similar buildings on the campus of Princeton University.

Retracing his steps back to the Neue Universitat, Bob continued to soak up the university atmosphere. He felt he was learning just by being there, as if he were absorbing knowledge through his skin.

Bob stopped at an outdoor café, ordered a coffee and strudel, and watched the parade go by. A multitude of young people, with backpacks and without. All hair colors and hairstyles. Groups of two, three, or four, striding along, going into one building or another. *This place is alive with learning,* Bob thought. It was very different from his experience at the City College of New York in upper Manhattan. Convent Avenue was nowhere near as exciting a town center as this. Later in his travels, Bob would experience the same atmosphere in the Latin Quarter of Paris at the Rue de Buci and nearby. It never failed to excite him.

Later, Bob was taken aback when he learned about the support that Heidelberg University heads had provided to the Nazi government after Hitler's rise to power in 1933. It marked a period of decline for the university that lasted through the end of World War II. During that period, fifty-nine out of 214 academics were expelled for racial or political reasons. The university and its heads cooperated with the Nazi government in other unfortunate ways as well.

At the time, Bob was just a young man seeing the world for the first time and not looking for things to criticize. He enjoyed seeing such places and enjoyed the company of the German people he met.

He finished his coffee, paid the bill, walked back to his car, and drove back to the barracks. He wondered if he would ever get the chance to live in a college town like Heidelberg, with access to learning and enlightened thought, and especially the same exciting atmosphere of youth he found here. It would be a nice way to live.

Bob did a quick three-mile run on the track near the ball field, then went back and relaxed on his bunk, waiting for the evening. After his visit to the university and soaking up the education vibe all afternoon, he started thinking back to his own education.

**High School Graduation at Loew's Paradise**

Bob's emotional attachment to his college experience was less than for high school. Starting college at age sixteen, two years younger than most, Bob found it difficult to connect and made only a few friends. Commuting to the City College of New York on Convent Avenue in upper Manhattan and returning to the Bronx on the subway each afternoon made creating friendships even more difficult. So, he let his mind drift back to high school and wander through the three enjoyable years that culminated in his high school graduation.

Bob had many pleasant memories of his experience at William Howard Taft High School on 170th Street and Sheridan Avenue. Living right across the street, he could run home for lunch and dash back to class when he heard the alarm bell announcing ten minutes to the start of the next class. Bob had many wonderful memories of the schoolyard: playing stickball, playing basketball, and running on the track. After play, there was always time at the Sugar Bowl restaurant on the corner of 170th Street and Morris Avenue, where you could get a pretzel and an egg cream – a chocolate soda with a dash of milk.

The high school academic program at Taft was good but not especially challenging. The kids were more interested in sports and music and cars. The students who tested strongly in math and science were usually sent to the Bronx High School of Science for its more rigorous math and science program.

Finally, after three enjoyable years, it was graduation year. The principal's graduation committee decided to have the graduation at Loew's Paradise on Grand Concourse, just south of Fordham Road. For Bronxites, seeing a movie at Loew's Paradise meant you were hitting the big time. You saved your money and went to a movie there for a special occasion.

In the Bronx, a first-run movie would start at Loew's Paradise or the RKO Fordham, then after a couple of weeks move on to the more ordinary local theaters like the RKO 167th Street, the Kent, or the Zenith on Jerome Avenue.

Seeing a movie at the Paradise was a truly upscale experience. It was an architecturally distinctive building that took up almost a whole city block. Such a large space could seat 4,000 guests. At the center near the top of the building was a clock, on top of which was a large statue of St. George on horseback, slaying the dragon. Once per hour, the horse would rear up and allow St. George to slay the dragon again.

After buying your tickets, you went through a set of bronze doors into an opulently furnished lobby, the ceiling of which was painted with murals. The auditorium itself was designed in the style of a $16^{th}$-century Italian Baroque garden. The ceiling was a deep blue with twinkling stars giving the appearance of summer moonlight. All in all, it was a truly spectacular and rich experience.

Bob's graduation was an important event for the Sievers. Although Bob's dad couldn't attend because he was sick, Sarah and Henry were both there, as were the families of all of Bob's friends.

The graduation seemed endless, but it went smoothly from beginning to end.

After countless boring speeches by the administrators, the valedictorian gave a good talk about the students striving to maximize their potential in life after graduation. He had already been accepted by Yale in pre-law.

Finally, the procession of students went up to receive their diplomas from the hand of the principal, and the graduation ceremony was over. Bob, Sarah, and Henry went to Krum's for ice cream sundaes, then headed home on the Concourse bus.

"Bob, Jake and I are so proud of you. When you start college in the fall, you will be the first Sievers to go to college," Sarah said proudly.

Henry added his congratulations but did not mention college. It was not something he had wanted for himself. Bob was happy to receive the compliment, but his mom's comment about him being the first Sievers to go to college only started sinking in later.

As he lay on his bunk at the Campbell Barracks that evening, back from his memories of his high school graduation, Bob thought about the importance of education and how it permeates every phase of people's lives, often setting them on a course to a better future. He thought about the feelings of empowerment, enablement, and positive energy that he'd gotten from his trip to Heidelberg University that day. He did not know it then, but much later he was destined to live in Princeton, New Jersey, a university town much like Heidelberg.

**Burning of the Castle**

Saturday arrived. Sergeant Major John Tucker was traveling, so Bob did not have to clean the Jeep. Bob slept late, and, after breakfast, ran five miles at the track near the ball field. He was happy he had quit the waiter job. It would have gotten him some more money but was more trouble than it was worth. He would have had to sacrifice his plan to stay in shape, too. Also, Frank's fiancée, Sandra Winter, had come from Los Angeles to stay for a couple of months and she'd brought along her friend Melissa Rogers. Bob had seen her picture and was looking forward to meeting her. Maybe they would hit it off and he would not want the extra work.

Everyone was excited to see their first Burning of the Castle.

They arrived on the bank of the Neckar opposite the castle at around 3 pm with blankets, picnic baskets, and drinks. They had to get there early because there were hordes of tourists in town and the "Burning" was the most popular event of the year. The extended family spread out on the blankets and had some snacks and beer, catching up while they waited for the festivities to begin.

The Burning of the Castle is a spectacular fireworks show put on several times per year to commemorate the destruction of the town and the castle by the French during the Nine Years' War of the late 1600s. The first time was in 1815 when European nobility gathered there to form an alliance against Napoleon. While people came from around the world and from neighboring communities to see it, Bob and his friends lived within a couple of miles.

They were facing the river with the castle on the opposite side, the best viewing area. By evening, small boats had arrived from both upriver and downriver. People had come from miles around. By dusk, hundreds of small boats were anchored in the river with their lights turned on. It was a festival of light, and the castle burning had not even started. The sky darkened. Night took over, but nothing happened. The sky was inky black, with many stars visible. The crowds got bigger, and the boats more densely crowded. The river's gentle current moved the boats from side to side, turning their lights into a moving light show.

The night wore on until around 9:30 or 10 pm when it began. The castle was suddenly illuminated in a reddish glow.

The castle was symbolically set afire as fire brigade volunteers ignited Bengal fires that bathed it in red light to simulate its destruction. After that, the fireworks began. Spectacular rockets rose to their peak and exploded in a multicolor extravaganza, sending shimmering particles hurtling toward earth. The darkness and the noise of the fireworks stopped any conversation. Boyfriends and girlfriends held hands, perhaps to signify that they were witnessing something unforgettable together. The fireworks continued until about 11 pm when slowly, in the suddenly deafening silence, small groups of the huge crowd started to leave the river bank and the boats slowly peeled off to return to their home berths. All was quiet as Bob and his little party waited for the crowds to dissipate. They were in no rush; the single soldiers living at the barracks were only about two miles from home.

They would talk about the evening for weeks afterward, knowing that they had seen one of Heidelberg's best offerings.

Bob was at the castle burning with Melissa. For Bob, it was love at first sight. She was small and slim. She had brown eyes and hair a lustrous brown, in a ponytail. She was easygoing and had a big, wide smile that radiated happiness.

They saw each other often after that first meeting. Melissa had recently graduated college and was working as a visiting nurse. It was easy to see why. She was a person who cared for others.

Melissa and Sandra had rented an apartment near the downtown area. While Sandra and Frank took some short trips to see Germany and France, Melissa stayed in Heidelberg. She and Bob saw each other often, meeting downtown for dinner, just walking around and enjoying the quaint and beautiful streets in the old town, or walking up on Philosopher's Walk where you could get an amazing view of the town and the castle from high on a hill on the opposite bank of the Neckar.

One night after dinner a couple of weeks later, they walked to Melissa's apartment for coffee. They sat back and talked about how they'd enjoyed the evening. They came closer and hugged. Bob could not resist. He kissed her deeply and started to unbutton her blouse.

She pulled back with a hurt expression on her face. "Do I have a choice?" she asked.

Bob was devastated. He let her go and grabbed her hands. "Of course, you do. Of course, you do." He looked into her eyes. "I didn't know. I thought you wanted to as much as me. Please forgive me."

The pained look on Bob's face enabled Melissa to forgive him on the spot, and their evening together continued pleasantly. Later, when Bob left, they kissed goodnight and agreed to see each other the next night. Bob knew all was forgiven.

A couple of weeks later, Melissa really did want to, so they became lovers as well as friends and spent much time together in the next few months. Bob's absence from the Enlisted Men's club did not go unnoticed by his friends.

**Oktoberfest**

With September's arrival, the time finally came to put the pea-green Beetle to its harshest test. The biggest festival in Germany, the Oktoberfest, was underway in Munich.

The largest beer festival and funfair in the world was three and a half hours from Bob's door. Starting in 1810, the fest now attracted six million people per year, from all over the world. In addition to the huge quantities of beer served, there were many fun attractions, including amusement rides and games.

The fest beer was said to be the best in the world. Brewed all year long, it was served only during the Oktoberfest, which ran for about two weeks from late September, ending on the first Sunday of October.

The opening of the fest happened in the same way each year. At noon, a 12-gun salute was followed by the tapping of the first keg by the mayor of Munich, who then pronounced "It's tapped." Bob wouldn't see this opening day ceremony, but he was happy to go at all.

Booking a room in Munich was impossible at that late date, so Bob decided to go for a day. Melissa had agreed to visit Paris with Sandra and Frank, so she could not go. None of Bob's friends would go for just a day, so he decided to go alone. Going solo, although not preferable, had its advantages. He could control the departure times and return whenever he wanted. He arranged for a pass for the last Friday in September because he had no Jeep duty on Saturday. Sergeant Major Tucker would be out of town at Baumholder, overseeing some Seventh Army matters. The schedule was tight because it was Charlie's birthday and there would be a party at the Enlisted Men's club that night to celebrate.

Friday morning came and Bob was ready. He had a full tank of gas and left at 6 am, right on schedule. He wanted to arrive by 10 am, park the car, and have as much time as possible at the fair before beginning the return trip at about 3 pm. It was an aggressive schedule that depended on things going right. Mostly, they did. *Hope for the best, prepare for the worst,* Bob thought.

Bob swung the Beetle out of Campbell Barracks and worked his way over to Speyerer Strasse, double-clutching to shift gears. He'd had the car serviced the previous week, so the oil and all the fluids were new. The Beetle turned onto Speyerer Strasse, headed southwest to the Autobahn, and easily merged onto the A5 headed south to Karlsruhe. With an effortless trip so far, Bob started to relax, hoping the Autobahn at this hour might be an easy ride with not too much traffic. At Karlsruhe, he turned onto the A8 heading southeast to Munich. The road started to change as it began a gradual ascent to 1,700 feet above sea level at Munich.

There was little traffic, so Bob stayed in the right lane, trying to not overextend the Beetle, not knowing what lay ahead. After another hour, he passed Stuttgart and continued on the A8. After a while, the road changed again and the elevation gain brought narrow winding roads with it. Bob got a little concerned about the winding road but it was dry and had very little traffic, and the Beetle was purring along.

Finally, at around 10 am, Bob arrived at the fairgrounds on the outskirts of Munich. Parking in a huge outdoor parking lot, Bob mentally surveyed the parking spot so he would be able to find it again. As he walked, he turned back to look at the car a couple of times to cement the location in his head. This mental trick would help him find the car again, even at 3 pm when the lot would be full.

*Not bad,* Bob thought. *If I leave at 3 pm, I will be back at 7 or 7:30, just in time for the birthday party.* A sense of relief settled in as he saw this would be a great day.

Entering the fair via the main gate, Bob walked down the main walkway and saw a dazzling view. The place was full of couples walking arm in arm and younger people in groups of six or eight. Literally hundreds of people were shoulder to shoulder, even so early in the day. On each side of the walkway were huge pavilions, some two stories tall, some taller, some with outdoor seating on the second floor. Some were simply giant tents filled with wooden picnic-type tables painted red. One tent alone could hold a thousand people. Bob was awed by the scale of the event. Several pavilions had big logos on top with the brand of the beer sponsoring the tent. Hofbräu, Paulaner, Lowenbrau, and others.

Bob walked along for about half a mile and entered the Hofbräu tent, where a band dressed in local country costumes was playing German music. The music was local folk music mostly, played on brass instruments. The noise of the crowd was deafening, and almost every table was full. Bob found a seat at a table with some Australians and ordered a liter stein of Hofbräu. The band was on a stage set on one side of the huge expanse of the tent. The music and the chatter created such a din that to order Bob just pointed to a beer stein on the table. The waiter nodded as if to say "Yes, sir. Be right back with your beer."

When the beer arrived, Bob took his first sip of the fest beer and knew the trip had been worth it. None of the local beers he had tasted could compare. Knowing he had to leave promptly at 3 pm, he ordered two more steins at once. The beer was smooth as silk with a wonderful flavor, more like a wine than beer. And no bitter aftertaste. Helped by the music, his Australian neighbors, and the wonderful taste of the beer, Bob soon got into the spirit. His neighbors were a group of eight Australian nurses who had decided to vacation together and see the Oktoberfest while they were in Germany. Before long, Bob had finished the first stein, and the other two steins arrived. He was glad he was drinking early so he would be alert for the trip back.

After finishing the third stein, Bob left the tent and continued down the walkway. Some of the buildings reminded him of the arcades he had seen at Coney Island as a kid. Ground floor arcades with huge overhead wooden swirls and panels advertising the name of the owner or product. He made a point of remembering one that advertised *Creperies, Kaffee, and Kuchen*. It was about 1 pm.

At an outdoor restaurant, Bob ate two small bratwurst sandwiches with a delicious mustard. He drank a liter of bottled water to wash them down and marveled at the size of the crowd as more and more people arrived.

*I have to return again when I can stay longer,* he thought.

Drawn by the music, he entered another tent. A group of dancers dressed in country costumes was performing a folk dancing show.

Finally, Bob walked back to the main avenue and stopped for coffee and apple cake at the place he had seen earlier. Then two things happened. His coffee and cake arrived, and a light rain started.

*Oh shit!* he thought.

He quickly called over the waitress, paid her in cash with a large tip, and got a to-go cup. He wrapped the cake in a napkin, put it in his pocket, and walked to the parking lot, drinking the coffee as he went. The coffee was delicious, strong, and hot.

Bob hated to leave while thousands were still there enjoying themselves, but he was concerned about the rain. He followed the mental breadcrumbs, found the Beetle, and swung out of the lot. Traffic was heavy now, with people both leaving and entering the fairgrounds. He traveled the short stretch to the highway, eased into the right lane, and headed back toward Stuttgart.

The light rain continued, and the road was wet. Bob drove slower than he had in the morning, but still hoped he would make it in time for the birthday party. The good news was that the gradual descent back to Stuttgart would be easier for the old car.

The rain picked up, making it harder to see through the windshield even though the newly replaced wiper blades worked fine. Bob and the pea-green Beetle continued along the mountain roads, winding and descending, winding and descending, traveling slowly, Bob's eyes glued to the road.

An hour went by and Bob started to feel better. He relaxed a little but kept his eyes glued to the road. Then, just before Stuttgart, ARRGH! CRASH! While traveling around a left turn in the road, the Beetle skidded and plowed into the guardrail on the right. As soon as the Beetle came to a stop, Bob turned off the engine.

"Shit," Bob cursed. "Shit, shit, shit."

He mentally took stock. *The car is damaged, may or may not be drivable. I'm OK. I didn't hit my head, just hit my side and shoulders against the steering wheel. Pain inside, too. Just some bruises but OK.*

After five minutes, Bob was sure he was not hurt. He got out of the car and checked the damage. The Beetle had bounced off the guardrail and faced forward again, on the shoulder. A lucky thing.

The front of the car was smashed in, and both front headlights were busted. No fluids were leaking from the underside of the car, though.

So far so good. The luckiest thing was the rear engine. Holy Cow! The smashed-in front was only the trunk.

*What now?* Bob thought. *I'm still 200 miles from Heidelberg. It will soon be dark, and the Beetle is blind. I need to get going.*

Just then, a German police car pulled over onto the shoulder behind Bob's car, its siren sounding. "Oh, shit," Bob cursed again. "This can't be good." The next piece of good luck was that there were no other cars or people involved in the accident. It was strictly the Beetle versus the guardrail. And the guardrail had won.

The Autobahnpolizei could see that Bob was sober. They were very polite and friendly. They took Bob's ID, saw that he was U.S. Army, and followed their protocol. They first checked the damage to the car to determine if it could be driven. It could! Then they wrote Bob a ticket for careless driving. They noted the headlights were not functioning and told Bob he had better get where he was going before dark. Then they left to continue their patrol.

Bob was ecstatic as he thought of all the bad outcomes that could have happened. After checking the steering, the brakes, and the engine compartment, he set off.

Driving even more slowly, Bob soon realized he would not get back before dark. By the time he eased around Stuttgart and merged onto the Autobahn going north to Heidelberg, dusk had faded into blackness and Bob could hardly see. Now the age-old question: what to do now?

Just north of Stuttgart, he pulled over onto the shoulder of the Autobahn to think. Finally, a strategy emerged.

"Thank goodness the tail lights work."

He pulled out into the right lane and headed north at about ten miles per hour. He could see only about ten feet in front of him.

Within a minute, a car came along in the left lane and zoomed past him. Bob sped up the Beetle to 45-50 mph and basked in the beautiful cone of light created by the car that had passed him. The Beetle followed closely in the slipstream of light for five or six miles until the visibility disappeared. As the light vanished, Bob slowed the car back down to ten mph and crawled along again, waiting eagerly for the next passer-by. This visibility dance took place about forty or fifty times, and Bob hoped all the while that no more German police patrols would spot him. Driving at night with no front headlights was surely another ticket or worse waiting to happen. Every time a car passed, Bob hoped it was not the Autobahnpolizei.

At around 11 pm, the driving nightmare finally ended. Bob exited the Autobahn at Heidelberg and made the short trip to Campbell Barracks under the protection of streetlamps all the way. At the ball field behind the barracks, he pulled the Beetle to a stop. It was battered and broken but still alive. Bob headed for his room. No one was there as they were still out celebrating Charlie's birthday.

On Monday morning, Bob reported to the captain in charge of the office and informed him of the accident. Bob could not let him be blindsided by hearing about it from the German police. Captain Hall was pissed off and read Bob the riot act.

"How many times have I told you? No incidents. No incidents No incidents. There is zero tolerance for this. You will lose your license for two months for sure. You are just lucky there were no German civilians injured or civilian property damage. You might have lost your license permanently. Now get out of here and get back to work. You will lose your license when the German police accident report arrives so get the car fixed now, while you can still drive."

Bob hightailed it out of Captain Hall's office and back to his desk. All his friends sympathized but mainly wanted to hear all the details of the trip and the accident. Bob repeated the story about a dozen times over the next week. He also took the car to a local repair shop, which replaced the front compartment and the front headlights for two hundred U.S. dollars, the same amount Bob had paid for the car originally.

Now was the time for Bob to count his blessings and think about what he could do without a car. He still felt lucky for all that he had experienced and all that he had done since he had left the South Bronx. Not driving a car for two months was a small price to pay. He smiled and thought about the recent conversations with his friends about Amsterdam, Paris, and Switzerland. Train travel was beckoning for the next few months.

Over dinner with Melissa, Bob told her all about the trip, bragging about his near-death experience on the Autobahn.

"Sounds exciting, but I am glad you are safe," Melissa said. She told Bob about Paris. They had visited the usual sights. Although she enjoyed Paris, Melissa had a bigger desire to visit Spanish-speaking countries. Having minored in Spanish in college, she was in love with the Spanish language and culture.

"I am so glad to know that," Bob said. "I studied Spanish for three years in high school. We should go to some Spanish-speaking countries together."

Melissa smiled with genuine happiness. Bob had come to see that she was as beautiful on the inside as on the outside. She read part of a romantic poem, and they made love right there on the sofa and went to sleep in each other's arms.

# Chapter Five – Amsterdam, Winter '67

November was an eventful month.

Planet Earth continued its relentless journey, tilting twenty-three and a half degrees from the plane of its orbit around the sun. It had reached that point in its journey when the Northern Hemisphere is furthest from the sun and colder weather arrives. The temperature in Heidelberg dropped to the forties, tourists became scarce, and the European winter loomed ahead.

Bob wondered at this. "I need to put gas in the Beetle's tank to travel, but the Earth does not need any fuel. It just goes on, propelled by some invisible force of nature."

Planning to travel, Bob and some of his bachelor friends knew they needed three things: money, time off, and warmer clothes.

For Bob, the money was there now, thanks to Aunt Yolande. Time off was no problem. Mostly three-day passes and an occasional week off. This time was well within the rules, and a small price for the generals to pay for keeping the military gears working smoothly in Europe. The group started shopping for some clothes.

On a trip downtown, several of them bought warm coats, sweaters, and gloves. Bob and Rich also bought simple point-and-shoot cameras. Bob had never owned a camera in his life. Another new adventure.

Bob had recently seen some tourists in town wearing ski jackets festooned with shield-shaped patches announcing places they'd visited. Not having traveled at all, Bob thought a jacket like that might keep him warm and be a great souvenir as well. So, he bought a green, quilted ski jacket that zipped up to his neck. That jacket, with the patches he sewed on, would become the symbol of Bob's European travels.

While downtown, they stopped at the train station and picked up some train schedules. The world beckoned. Heidelberg was the very center of a circular universe with a several-hundred-mile radius that included Amsterdam, Paris, Berlin, and Switzerland.

Bob and his friends felt good about contributing to the Vietnam War effort by keeping things running smoothly in Europe. It made them feel better about their "entitled" status. Bob especially appreciated his job with the Seventh Army, the wall of tanks that kept Russia out of Western Europe. Nukes were out of the question, so the fearsome M60 (Patton) tank kept Europe safe and allowed the U.S. to focus on Vietnam.

But President Johnson was worried now. His Great Society program had had many achievements: desegregation, voting rights, Medicare. However, those good works were being eroded by failure in Vietnam. In October 1967, hundreds of thousands of war protesters gathered for demonstrations in New York City and Washington, D.C.

In November, President Johnson called General Westmoreland, his commander of the armed forces in Vietnam, to Washington to reassure himself and the American people. The general explained that the U.S. was winning. Although the campaigns so far were having little effect, he explained that they had entered into a war of attrition and would win eventually.

Along with millions of Americans back home, Bob and his friends were relieved to hear this because they too were uneasy. Behind the façade of their life of privilege, they knew, in the back of their minds where all the fears and emotions are, that the good life could end tomorrow. Despite having less than one year to serve, the normal threshold for a reassignment, their service could be extended and they could be sent to Vietnam the next day.

"Hope for the best, prepare for the worst, but enjoy life now," was their mantra.

In the last week of October, Bob was called into Sergeant Major Tucker's office.

"The Seventh Army is going on two weeks of maneuvers next week, and I need your help for a few days," Tucker said.

"No problem," Bob answered. "I'll clear it with Captain Hall and be ready to go." He was excited. His first real job for the Seventh Army.

Tucker smiled. "Thanks, Bob. I want you to spend two days at Kaiserslautern, helping to set up the tactical command post for the maneuvers."

The Seventh Army staged maneuvers several times a year. They did this to show everyone that they were ready and that the tanks could roll. They had to show this to the Russians, to allies, and to the folks back in America. Those two weeks were a time of excitement and crazed, hectic activity that usually ended with a sense of relief and a celebration.

A tactical command post provides the communications and logistics support for a short-term military operation. It is a forward base to control operations at the front line and ensure communications between headquarters and the troops in the field.

An operational military command post requires a secure location, all kinds of communications gear, secure telephone lines, mobile radios, and a variety of office supplies. For these maneuvers, the Seventh Army would use the U.S. Army barracks at Kaiserslautern, about 50 miles southwest of Heidelberg. The Seventh Army soldiers would be nearby, bivouacked in tents with the Patton tanks standing by. Sergeant Major Tucker was the operations sergeant major responsible for all aspects of the command post.

Bob left for Kaiserslautern that Monday. Representing Tucker, he worked with Operations Sergeant Smith to set up the command post. The communications included landline telephones as well as secure wireless radios. After unpacking the wireless radios and setting the correct frequencies, Bob and Sergeant Smith thoroughly tested the communications. They called various rooms at the command post, then Bob drove out to the bivouac area to test the wireless radios with Sergeant Smith back at the command post.

"Can you hear that the Seventh Army is on the move?" Bob said to Sergeant Smith from the bivouac area.

"Loud and clear, Bob. Loud and clear," said Sergeant Smith.

Then, from the CP, Bob called the corporal in Sergeant Major Tucker's office in Heidelberg to test the landline. All worked fine.

They retested the comms the next day, and all was still working fine. Then Bob set up the Situation Room for analog battle tracking. He unpacked the whiteboards, situation maps, markers, and clear plastic tabletop. Hard copies of all maneuver orders were placed in a secure file cabinet. Finally, a security schedule was established with rotating shifts of guards to secure the area.

Now that the command post was set up and ready to go, Bob telephoned Sergeant Major Tucker to give him the status.

"How is it going?" Tucker asked when he got on the line.

"Sergeant Major, the command post is operational," Bob reported.

Tucker was silent for a moment. Then he asked, "Bob, are you committing to this? I am personally coming out there tomorrow to verify everything before the exercise begins."

"Yes, Sergeant Major," Bob replied. "The command post is operational." He knew that was the only acceptable reply.

"Good job, Bob," Tucker said. "Come on home then."

"It has arrived," Captain Hall said on Bob's return to the office the next day. He called Bob into his office and explained that the German police paperwork about his accident had arrived. Bob's driver's license was now officially suspended for two months.

The captain repeated what he had said before. "You are damn lucky there were no civilian injuries, so suck it up and make the best of it."

Bob pretended to be upset for Captain Hall's benefit, but he was excited in the emotional part of his brain. This suspension, along with the money from Aunt Yolande, was his ticket to travel for the next few months. It was perfect timing since Heidelberg was much less exciting in the winter with fewer tourists visiting and students heading home for the holidays.

"Yes, sir. I'm sure I can do that, sir," Bob replied.

As Bob turned to go, Captain Hall stopped him. "By the way, how did it go at Kaiserslautern?"

"The command post is up and running, sir. It went off without a hitch," Bob said.

"Excellent," Hall said. "You know that the Seventh Army is the key to our defense of Europe? They're keeping us all safe here."

"Yes, sir, I know it," Bob replied.

Bob went back to his desk to get some work done. Two new Line of Duty investigations had come in while he was away, and he had to get started on them before taking off on a three-day pass the next weekend. These investigations were lengthy and needed to be started immediately.

The first involved an auto accident in Hamburg that killed a U.S. Army lieutenant on a three-day pass. The second was a bar fight in Munich in which a corporal was injured.

There were requests for police reports, hospital reports, lab reports, and photographs if available, as well as the soldier's personnel file. In death cases, autopsy reports, and death certificates were needed. Many times, coordination with the Administrative Law Division was necessary if some necessary police or other reports were not obtainable. The military higher-ups would have to obtain them by other means.

There were also consequences for the soldier or the soldier's family. An injury or death found to be "Not In Line of Duty, Due to Own Misconduct" could deprive the soldier or survivors of critically needed benefits during a difficult time.

The army's initial presumption was always that the soldier's disease, injury, or death was "In Line of Duty." But then a thorough investigation was made. That investigation would have to find substantial evidence to overturn that presumption. The evidence would have to show intentional misconduct or willful negligence to warrant a negative finding.

Bob spent the next two days starting to make all the various contacts and requests for information to begin these investigations. No lunches and no Enlisted Men's club. When such events happen, nothing is more important than initiating the investigations. He had to have everything done to be able to take his three days off at the end of the week.

In his spare moments, he and Charlie planned their trip to Amsterdam. Charlie had decided to propose to his girlfriend Linda back home in Boston, Massachusetts, and he needed a ring. What better place to buy it than Amsterdam?

Heidelberg was at the center of a convenient travel circle that had a precision train service and the Autobahn at its heart. In Germany, the sun might not shine on any given day, but the trains would run on time. That was for certain.

With the overnight train, you could sleep on the train, arrive early in the morning, and have a full first day. The overnight train was the way to maximize the value of a three-day pass. The proximity of great destinations made the three-day pass one of the most valuable commodities in a location like Heidelberg. And because the pass contained a start date and time and end date and time, you could plan your trip precisely.

Of course, you had to do everything within those 72 hours. Other than in the normal course of a day, if a soldier was gone outside those 72 hours, he was AWOL and subject to serious punishment by the military.

So, Charlie and Bob arranged to leave for Amsterdam on Friday. They had three-day passes signed and approved by Captain Hall, from 2100 hours Friday (9 pm) to 2100 hours Monday. The train from Heidelberg to Amsterdam would leave at 10:02 pm and arrive in Amsterdam at about 9 am. You could count on it.

On Friday evening, with one bag each, Charlie and Bob rode to the Bahnhof in Rich's old Ford.

Rich dropped them off. "Don't do anything I wouldn't do," he said.

"But Rich, that's why we are going," Bob joked.

"We are just going for the ring," Charlie said.

"Yeah, right," Rich replied. "Next time, I'll have to go along to watch over you guys."

At 9:45, they boarded the train and found seats in second class, the least expensive way to travel.

"Least expensive way, sir," became their mantra as the travel miles piled up that winter.

Vreeeeooooeeeeoooo! The train whistle's high-pitched howl sounded at precisely 10:02 pm. The train slowly came to life and shuddered out of the station, quickly picking up to a speed of about 50 miles per hour. The second-class compartment was noisy, and the clackety, clackety, clack sound made it hard to talk. However, being an overnight trip, it was less crowded than during the day. They spread out and tried to get some sleep. The next day would be long and exciting.

Outside the train, the night was dark. You could not see into the blackness unless the train was going through a town. Bob thought about the next day. This trip was his first real visit to an international city except for Frankfurt, where he hadn't gotten to see the sights.

His mind focused on all the new things he would experience the next day, and then he relaxed. Seeing the small towns pass by reminded him of the bungalow colony in the Catskills. He thought about the white bungalows and his family – Aunt Yolande and Uncle Warner, his cousins Pam and Dave, his brother Henry – and how they lived in a sort of compound, each to their own bungalow along with some other friends from their Bronx neighborhood.

In the late afternoons, the folks would sit outside, each group to their own picnic table but also together, on the quadrangle of grass between the bungalows. Bob remembered playing ball on the grass with the other kids while dinner was being made. Bob's mother finished cooking dinner and called them inside.

Bob did not know Pam and Dave so well because they were several years older. At age eight or nine, a three-year age difference was a lifetime. They would become friends much later, when the age difference meant a lot less.

The property was huge. Sometimes before dinner, a group would walk along the road to the entrance, and then even out onto the country road that led to town. It was peaceful and quiet. Just the insects buzzing as the sun dropped in the late afternoon sky. It was a good time to be a nine-year-old.

Bob was startled out of his reverie when the train passed Leverkusen, a suburb of Koln (Cologne). The sky lit up in a brilliant yellow glow.

Leverkusen was the home of the Bayer company. About a quarter of a mile from the train there stood a 40-foot-high Bayer Aspirin, all lit up, dotted with yellow incandescent bulbs. It had the exact shape and wording of a Bayer Aspirin. It was like a brilliant harvest moon coming right toward the train, gigantic and almost close enough to touch. On all future trips to Amsterdam, that became Bob's signpost, a lighthouse marking the halfway point to Amsterdam.

The towns drifted by on the almost straight corridor to Amsterdam. They stopped in Dusseldorf, and later in Arnhem. Between the towns, there was only inky blackness. Bob and Charlie were startled awake when they arrived at Centraal Station in Amsterdam at 9 am on Saturday morning. They had dozed off and on during the night, but now shook off the sleep, ready for the day. They got off the train and walked with their bags through the station.

Outside, they looked up at the beautiful station façade. The building was of a beautiful Dutch Neo-Renaissance architecture, built in 1889 on three artificial islands.

Amsterdam's Centraal Station was a European travel hub with connections to trains, buses, and ocean-going ships. Every day, tens of thousands of people filtered through on their way somewhere else or, as for Bob and Charlie, arrived at their destination.

The street was quiet at this hour on a Saturday, but there were bike racks with hundreds of bikes at the ready, just awaiting their owners' return. Amsterdam, being totally flat, was a biker's dream.

The city was designed perfectly for tourists. The Centraal Station was located right in the center of a spider web of canals radiating outward from the station. It made for easy walking, and easy sightseeing by canal boat. Any other places could be reached by the many trams traveling back and forth on the streets.

At a hostel about two blocks from the station, they booked two nights. For about $32.00 each, they got a very small room with a bath down the hall. They carried their bags up the long, steep staircase. After a quick look at the room and the bath, they were out the door by 10 am. Only thirteen hours of the seventy-two used, and Charlie and Bob were on the move in Amsterdam!

"Let's do it all," Bob said.

Seated in a nearby coffee shop, they each drank a delicious, strong coffee with a large sweet roll and planned the day.

"We have two full days," Chuck said. "48 hours. The diamond ring is first, then the red-light district."

They both smiled. Neither of them was very experienced in sex or love.

"Are you sure about the diamond," Bob asked. "It sounds serious. And expensive. What if it doesn't work out with Linda?"

"I am totally sure," Chuck said. "We have known each other since we were seventeen. In the year I've been away, we have been writing steadily. No, the diamond is for sure. I have arranged a seven-day leave, and I'm booked on a flight to Boston next week. I'm going to propose to Linda then."

"OK," Bob said. "I hope you know what you are doing. So, we want to get to the diamond place by 2 o'clock. That will give us plenty of time to get back, shower, and grab something to eat."

"Then the red-light district tonight," Charlie interrupted.

They both smiled knowing smiles although neither of them knew anything about what to expect there.

They left the coffee shop at 11 with plenty of time on their hands.

They walked around the nearer canals, Singel and Herengracht, and marveled at the cleanliness. They looked at the canal houses as they walked by, noticing the stepped roofs and the red and orange brick. The canal houses were very vertical, and most had large hooks jutting out from the top floor. The hooks were the only way to get furniture to the upper floors, they had read.

By noon, they were hungry, so they found a tram going to Leidseplein. People at the hostel had told them to go there to eat. The trams were fun and efficient. You could see all the action on the streets as you went by. Much better than the confined feeling of the underground subways Bob was used to in the Bronx. They boarded at the rear of the tram and bought a day ticket from the conductor.

**Leidseplein**

Despite having heard that Leidseplein was a happening place, they were amazed when they got off the tram there. A *plein* in Amsterdam is similar to a square in English.

Leidseplein was one of the busiest places for nightlife in the city, located along the Singelgracht near the center of the city. All the side streets were packed with restaurants and nightclubs. The Stadsschouwburg (municipal theater) dominated one corner of the square. There were old cast-iron-looking buildings with mansard roofs.

It was a beautiful Saturday, windy and sunny with a blue sky and a few small, white clouds. People were strolling everywhere, and there were outdoor cafés galore with tables and colorful umbrellas to block the sun. A woman, wearing a headscarf as protection from the wind, passed by with a baby stroller. Bicycles and bike racks were everywhere, as were younger kids throwing frisbees. The square teemed with life and excitement. A band was playing in the middle of the square as strollers walked by.

They ate lunch at an outdoor café. Music was coming from a jukebox inside. Jefferson Airplane's "Somebody to Love." Then, The Box Tops' "The Letter," just released in August. The streets were awash with the sound that captured the restlessness of youth.

In April, Jefferson Airplane had released their most influential album, *Surrealistic Pillow,* which included "Somebody to Love."

Although Amsterdam long had the reputation of being slow to pick up on counterculture, it seemed to have caught on to the vibe much quicker in 1967. It had quickly adopted the bohemian counterculture that developed as a youthful rebellion against the post-World War II and cold war mindset. The movement had spread from Paris' Saint-Germain-des-Prés in the 1950s to Carnaby Street in London in the early '60s to Haight Ashbury in San Francisco, where Jefferson Airplane ruled the roost for the moment.

"We should definitely return here for dinner," Bob said.

Charlie agreed.

**The Diamond**

They had scheduled a 2 pm tour of the De Vries diamond center, where diamonds are cut and polished.

De Vries had started up more recently than some of the more established companies, which had started right after the end of World War II. It was located in an old factory building not far from the hotel, so they just walked there.

"Maybe we'll get a better price there," Charlie said.

At De Vries, they attended a one-hour tour that covered the history of diamonds as well as Amsterdam's diamond history. It was one time called the "Diamond City." But as 95% of the diamond cutters were Jewish, almost all of them fled or were killed by the Nazis during World War II. Although the diamond industry in Amsterdam never again reached the prestige of its former heyday, some important businesses prospered again after the war.

They saw diamonds being cut and polished and learned all about how they are valued. That is, the four Cs: carats, color, clarity, and cut. They learned about the "brilliant cut" or "Amsterdam cut" as it became known.

"Wow," Charlie said after the tour. "We are diamond experts now."

"Just in time, too, for Linda's sake," Bob agreed.

Charlie smiled.

After the tour, they were guided to the shop, and a salesperson showed them a variety of loose diamonds that could be set in a ring in only thirty minutes.

"Why are you buying a diamond?" the salesperson asked. "The more I know, the more help I can be."

"It's an engagement ring," Charlie replied.

"And how much can you spend?" the salesperson asked.

"Two thousand U.S. dollars."

"All right," said the salesperson. "Let me show you some diamonds."

With a $2,000 budget, there were only a few choices to make, mainly the type of cut. The other features were pretty much the same for that price range. For example, the fewer internal flaws, the more expensive the diamond. So for $2,000, most of the diamond's characteristics were within a very narrow band.

Charlie was excited, and the diamond purchase train was barreling along to its station. He chose a "brilliant" cut round diamond, which was the most popular. It was small, but it looked beautiful after it was polished and set in a white gold ring.

"Charlie," Bob said. "You are headed for the altar for sure. No girl could resist that."

Charlie just smiled.

To the four Cs, De Vries added a fifth C for confidence. Along with the diamond ring, they gave Charlie a certificate from the IGI (International Gemological Institute), which was actually a report, grading the diamond's quality.

It was about 4:30 by then, so they walked back to the hostel to freshen up before dinner. They realized that the diamond ring would be with them 24 hours per day for the next two days. There was no place else the ring would be safe. Charlie was excited, and he floated along as they walked back, feeling like the master of his own fate.

To save money, they decided not to go back to Leidseplein that evening. Instead, they located an inexpensive-looking Indonesian restaurant near the hostel and both had rijsttafel, something they had never heard of before, along with Amstel Beer on tap.

Rijsttafel is the Dutch word for "rice table." For about 100 years, the Dutch, masters of commerce, shipbuilding, and sailing, dominated the world economy. Indonesia was one of their colonies, and the food was brought back to Holland.

A rijsttafel dinner revolves around a center dish of rice, with many small dishes to show off the variety of unique flavors of the cuisine.

Bob and Charlie's smallish table was crowded with a big bowl of white rice surrounded by about twelve small plates of meat satays, vegetable satays in a peanut sauce, beef in coconut curry sauce, and crunchy banana fritters. There was also roasted coconut and some kind of pickled vegetables to cleanse the palate. It was a mind- and palate-opening experience for two guys used to the cheeseburgers and fries at the Enlisted Men's club in Heidelberg.

On the way back, they stopped at a coffee shop to wait until 10 pm when they would head over to see the red-light district.

They talked about the trip, the diamond, and Charlie's upcoming trip to Boston to pop the question to Linda. Most importantly, the main mission of the trip was already accomplished. Now Charlie just had to hang on to the diamond until he could put it on Linda's finger.

"You have to use a zero-trust policy, Charlie," Bob said. "The ring stays in your pocket 24/7 until you put it on Linda's finger. You can't mess around with this. Agreed?"

"Agreed," Charlie replied.

"Are you sure you know what you are doing? Any girl would love to have that diamond, but why would she want you?" Bob joked.

Charlie laughed. "I am very sure. She has given me all the signs."

The coffee was strong and full of flavor, as strong as a Columbian roast but much smoother.

"It has to do with the way we brew it," the waiter explained. "We brew the coffee in cold water for three to six hours. The lack of oxidation makes it much smoother to the taste and very flavorful."

Charlie and Bob smiled at each other. They were becoming men of the world.

**The Red-Light District**

Sometime after 10 pm, they left the coffee shop and walked the short distance to the red-light district. It was located in the heart of downtown, not far from the hostel and Centraal Station. When Bob and Charlie entered the district, they were taken aback by the whole scene. First of all, that sex for pay was legal here was unbelievable to two inexperienced young fellows, one from the Bronx, the other from Boston.

Their senses were bombarded by the neon lights and the array of colors everywhere. A series of row houses had parlor floors awash in pink and lavender lighting. Most of the parlor windows had women standing or sitting in plain sight in various stages of undress, advertising their services. It was like a gigantic spice market with all the beautiful colors and aromas. There were neon signs at ground floor level, advertising peep shows, sex shops, and various cafés.

It was a kaleidoscope of color and activity that neither of them had ever seen. They walked around the streets for about an hour, taking it all in. Although it was forbidden to take photographs of the women in the windows, Bob's camera was small and he had to try it. Hiding most of the camera behind the flap of his jacket, he took several photographs, which he claimed would "forever remain hidden in my photograph collection."

Because their most important mission had become protecting the diamond, they reluctantly walked back to the hostel and turned in for the night.

On Sunday morning, Bob and Charlie packed for the day, making sure the diamond was safe in Charlie's backpack. After breakfast of coffee and a couple of sweet rolls at a coffee shop, they walked over to the Centraal Station. Right there at Prins Hendrikkade were several canal tour boats ready to depart on the next hour. For $10, they bought a 24-hour pass on the canal boat where you could "hop on and hop off." This was a highlight of the trip.

Amsterdam's 165 canals were created over the centuries to provide transport, reclaim land, and expand the city. On a map, the ring of canals looked like a belt of concentric circles with the Centraal Station at the center.

The tour boat, long and low-slung, was able to travel under the many bridges of the city. It had a glass ceiling and many open windows for easy viewing. Beautiful scenery passed by, including the famous canal houses with their Neo-Renaissance stepped roofs and many colors of brick. They saw one of the world's narrowest houses, which was probably built in an alley between two houses. A guide spoke in five different languages as the boat sailed along. They never knew if it was a person or a recording.

The boat stopped at many of the city's attractions. They hopped off at Leidseplein for lunch and to walk around there again. After another coffee, they hopped back aboard the canal boat to finish the tour, finally arriving back at Centraal Station in the evening. They were exhausted but happy. They had accomplished their mission. They had seen Amsterdam, the red-light district, and most importantly, had bought a respectable diamond with a top-flight pedigree right from the "Diamond City."

After an early dinner, they flopped in the room for the night.

**Bicycles Everywhere**

On Monday morning, they were back at Centraal Station at 9 am, ready to board the 9:30 train back to Heidelberg. There they saw an incredible sight. Hundreds of people were on their way to work on bicycles. Bicycles everywhere.

Despite the large number of bicycles, it wouldn't be until the early to mid-1970s that Amsterdam would truly become one of the bicycle capitals of the world. Cars were still dominant in Amsterdam in the 1960s. But when traffic accidents and deaths peaked in 1971, things began to change. After the quadrupling of oil prices in 1973, the people of Amsterdam got serious. Bicycle routes were created everywhere and traffic-free days became commonplace.

While Charlie was used to seeing some bicycles in the Boston area, Bob was taken aback. There was nothing like this in the South Bronx.

On the train, Bob thought about all the bicycles he had just seen. It affected him in the same way as when he had seen the dance floor at the Enlisted Men's club. He was suddenly shocked that he had never owned or ridden a bike in his 24 years. He had found yet another thing to make up for, and he was determined to embrace it. On returning home, Bob learned to ride in Forest Park in Queens, where his brother Henry was living at the time.

The train ride back to Heidelberg was way more interesting than the ride to Amsterdam. In daylight, they could see the lush countryside, flat in Holland but becoming more undulating as the train crossed into Germany and on to Heidelberg. The German landscape was very green and dotted with farms as they traveled further south, beyond Koln.

They arrived back at the barracks well inside the three-day pass window. No one really clocked you in at Campbell Barracks; they didn't need to. Like most things in the military, they didn't watch you closely, but if you were involved in an unfortunate incident outside your window and thus considered AWOL, well, then it was your ass.

Bob and Charlie, now two international travelers, showered, shaved, and headed to the Enlisted Men's club. They could hardly wait to tell the story. Over cheeseburgers and fries, they told the others the story of "Charlie's Brilliant Diamond" and all the rest.

But Bob should have been concerned about his own love life instead of Charlie's. The next day, he met Melissa at her and Sandra's apartment. Frank's fiancée, Sandra, knew her time was up, so she had gone back to Los Angeles. Melissa had decided to stay for another month to give Bob and her a little more time to work things out.

They went to dinner that night, and Melissa explained her unhappiness. She loved Bob dearly but needed him to love her back and to make a commitment. Bob loved her too, as he had told her and shown her so many times over the past few months. After just a couple of months with Melissa, he saw that she loved him for himself and only wanted to be with him.

But Bob had worries too. His life was just beginning. He did not know what he would do after the army. He did not know if he would earn enough to have a family. He was afraid of disappointing her. He also was aware that he knew nothing about life and had so much to learn on his journey. He could not make the commitment.

Finally, two weeks later, Melissa told Bob she was going back to Los Angeles.

Bob took her to the train station for the trip to Frankfurt and a flight home. They hugged, and both cried. He told her he would visit, but he knew it was not true. His heart was broken, but Amsterdam had shown him clearly that his life was just beginning.

Bob came to regret that decision. For a long time after, he could not think of Melissa without the pain of thinking about how nice a life they could have had together. While his life went on to have many interesting chapters, he always knew he had done the one thing that no one should ever do – turn your back on true love. For a long time, Bob consoled himself with a thought he had read somewhere: *If something good existed, even if only for a brief time, then it still existed.*

With Melissa having gone back to Los Angeles, Bob and his friends were ready to step up their travels.

# Chapter Six – Paris, Winter '67

December came and brought the first snow with it. There was a light dusting in Heidelberg, with portents of more to come. It was bleak but beautiful at the same time. Bob and Arnie went downtown. They walked up to Philosopher's Walk, at the top of the hill on the opposite side of the river from the castle. There were a few other walkers there, dressed in winter jackets and gloves.

The bright, multicolored scene of the summer was gone. The Neckar was calm but gray. The copper-colored rooftops were now white. It was a gray and white day. An overhanging mist limited visibility, turning Heidelberg into a Christmas card come to life. Snowflakes drifted lower in the sky and settled on roofs, lampposts, and people's faces. The roadway of the old bridge was covered with snow, looking almost white, while the sides kept their brown color. Arnie and Bob took some photos and headed back down to the Leipzigger on Untere Strasse.

After a couple of beers, they headed back to the base. That night was an Enlisted Men's club night. The Zaras, the popular Spanish band, was back from Spain and playing another tour of Europe. Everyone wanted to hear them.

Bob walked over to the PX to call home. He had not spoken to his mother since the loan from Aunt Yolande had come through. On Saturday afternoon, he could usually reach her right away. But not this time. He had to try several times before he finally connected. They talked for a long time.

Bob told her how grateful he was for the money. "Please tell Aunt Yolande," he added.

"You should call her yourself," Sarah replied. She gave him Yolande's telephone number.

"The trip to Amsterdam was great," he said. He told Sarah about the diamond purchase and the rijsttafel dinner. "I learned so much. It was a great use of the money."

He wanted to reassure her and Yolande that the money was being used well. He conveniently forgot to tell her about the auto accident returning from Munich and the visit to the red-light district in Amsterdam.

He said that he and three friends were planning to visit Paris next, and told her how excited he was to try speaking French after studying it for two years.

"I'm glad you're enjoying it over there. But just be careful, too," Sarah said.

"Of course, Mom. I always am," he reassured her. "How is Henry?"

"He is good. He likes his work, and they like him. He has moved to Queens, to his own apartment. I don't know why. I told him he could stay with me and save some more money, but he refused."

Bob rolled his eyes but said nothing.

There was no word yet on her move to Co-Op City, but she told Bob she would keep him posted. "It probably won't happen before you return," she said.

She'd gotten a raise at Ohrbach's. They wanted her to work full time. She refused, but they gave her the raise anyway. Bob promised to call more often, and they said goodbye.

The Enlisted Men's club was crowded. Bob, Rich, Frank, and Arnie were there with five or six others. Dinner was over, and a bridge game was underway. The show would begin soon.

Having decided to go to Paris, Bob, Rich, Frank, and Arnie were planning the details. The Amsterdam trip had proved the method, so they could just concentrate on the specifics. They decided to leave two Fridays from then with a three-day pass. They would take an overnight train trip to Paris, arriving at the Gare de l'Est on Saturday morning. They each promised to have their work done so Captain Hall would sign off on the passes.

The club got crowded, and the Zaras opened their act. There were five musicians and a lead singer, Julie.

The crowd always loved the Zaras' music. *Sgt. Pepper's Lonely Hearts Club Band* was still very popular, so they played "With a Little Help from My Friends."

The set continued with "To Sir with Love," followed by "The Letter" by the Box Tops, and the amazing "Gimme Some Lovin'" by the very popular Spencer Davis Group.

The dance floor was packed with people moving to the music. After the second set, people started drifting out. Another fantastic evening at Campbell Barracks.

The next two weeks went smoothly, and the date for the Paris trip arrived. They got a ride to the Heidelberg Bahnhof and boarded the 10 pm train for Paris. It was cold, in the forties, so they brought warm coats. Bob wore his green quilted ski jacket, which now had its first patch, the one he'd bought in Amsterdam.

They got into the second-class compartment, and the train departed at precisely 10 pm. It was a short hop south to Karlsruhe. There, they changed trains, got into a similar second-class compartment, and traveled due west to Paris.

They chatted for a while about the office, life back home, and what they might do when they returned. They all had about the same time left in service, about ten months. After the news stories in November about how the U.S. was winning the war, they all agreed the odds were good they would return home on time.

"I guess Sandra and I will get married," Frank said. "I am planning to work in my family's Chevrolet dealership.

Muscle cars are becoming the rage in the Los Angeles area, so I'll get rich and open my own dealership."

"Wow," said Bob. "I wish I were that sure. I really don't know what I'll do. I guess I'll have to wing it when I get back."

"I'll go to Florida," Arnie said. "I'm tired of Dallas. I have a brother in the insurance business in Jacksonville, and I'll go to work with him."

"You lucky dog," Rich remarked. "I'm going back to Cleveland, so no warm winters for me. I studied journalism and I'll go into the newspaper business."

Bob told them about the Amsterdam trip again, especially about the diamond and the red-light district. The others couldn't believe Charlie and Bob hadn't partaken at the red-light district and laughed at the story. They all agreed there was no red-light district in Paris. Without a project like buying a diamond, they were free to use all their energies to see Paris.

"I wonder how it is going for Charlie in Boston with Linda?" Bob mused aloud.

"He says they have known each other forever," Rich said. "He'll be fine."

They all agreed.

The only four in the compartment, they drifted to sleep. Other than the stops in towns, there was only the darkness of night and the occasional whistle of the train to disturb them.

The shrill train whistle as the train slowed to its final destination at Gare de l'Est awakened them at about 5 am. They got off the train and walked out of the station, with one bag each. Bob had told them how traveling light had made it easy to get around Amsterdam. They had all understood, and decided to do the same.

They walked through the cavernous main hall of the train station. The Gare de l'Est is the main terminus at the eastern end of Paris, connecting Paris with eastern France. There was a plaque describing the importance of the station in World War I when large numbers of French troops were transported to the front from there.

They emerged from the station on Boulevard de Strasbourg in the 10th arrondissement, the north-central part of the city. They walked a couple of blocks and found a cheap hotel on the Rue Chabrol, just minutes from the train station.

They took two rooms. An old elevator took them up two floors, where the rooms were next to each other. Bob and Arnie shared one room, and Rich and Frank the other. They were small, old-fashioned rooms with wallpaper peeling off the walls and old bathroom fixtures. In Bob's room, an old chair with a rattan seat was near the window. The bed's headboard was a mahogany wood, as was the set of drawers.

The rooms each had large windows overlooking the street. The windows opened wide, affording a big view of the street and the action there.

It was cheap, but everything worked and they had the minimum they needed. And they were in Paris! They were ready to enjoy the city by 9:30 thanks to the magic of the three-day pass and the incredibly reliable European train system.

The location was perfect. On foot, they were one hour from the Eiffel Tower, thirty minutes from Île de la Cité, the heart of Paris, and thirty minutes from Montmartre.

Eager to get started, the four musketeers left the hotel and stopped at a local Banque Nationale de Paris to exchange currency.

The French franc had been devalued in 1960 and was now worth about 25 cents each. So about four francs per U.S. dollar. It wouldn't be until 1999 that the euro would replace the franc.

They changed a few hundred dollars into French francs and were on their way. They walked about forty minutes to the Seine and arrived at Pont de l'Alma on the right bank, not far from the Eiffel Tower.

Bob was excited to finally be able to speak French after studying it for two years in college. He became the group's spokesman. At first, he was horrible, but he steadily improved. He remembered his professor's parting advice:

"If you only remember one thing, remember this phrase: Comment vous dire en français?"

Translation: "How do you say in French?" Then you give them a word in your language. So, "Comment vous dire en français restaurant?" means "How do you say restaurant in French?" Bob used this extensively at the beginning. Not only did he start to learn more French, but he had a ready-made excuse to speak to the French people he met.

Although he had heard the French were not friendly, Bob did not find that to be the case. Far from it, he found that the more he reached out by trying to speak French, which he did very poorly, the more they extended themselves back toward him trying to be helpful. In his few days in Paris, Bob began to feel more comfortable with the language and the people. He bought a copy of *Le Monde,* the popular newspaper, to read on the train trip back. He didn't understand every word, but he got the gist of many articles.

They bought tickets for a three-hour boat tour on a *Bateaux Mouches* and sat back to enjoy the show. Their first view of the city was incredibly beautiful. The bateau traveled up the Seine and then back, passing right by some of the most important sights: the Eiffel Tower, the Louvre, Notre-Dame de Paris, the Conciergerie. The audio guide coming from below decks explained the sights in eight languages, so it took some time to hear it in English. Bob was listening for both the English and the French to try to learn more French.

Back at Pont de l'Alma, they left the boat and walked along the left bank. Bob, a photographer now, stopped to take a beautiful photo of the Eiffel Tower from a distance along the Rue de l'Université, a well-known postcard shot. As a new photographer, he took all the rookie photographs and had the others photograph him in front of all the monuments. He later called this group of photos *The You Were There Album.*

They walked through Saint-Germain-des-Prés and stopped at a café for coffees and croissants.

It was a cold, gray day. The temperature was in the high forties, too cold to sit outside. The street was crowded with people walking by. They went in and sat at a small table right by the large window. It was the perfect table, outside but inside at the same time.

The waiter came over, and Bob ordered. "Quatre double et quatre croissants, s'il vous plaît."

The waiter seemed happy to be getting the order in French, and the coffees arrived quickly.

"Merci," Bob said. Arnie, Rich, and Frank were happy to have a translator, as faulty as Bob was.

They sat with their coffees and watched the people passing by. The café was nicely situated on a narrow street, Rue Guisarde. The large picture window opened wide onto the street so they could see the passers-by.

The conversation turned to Vietnam. They were all in the same boat: each had ten or eleven months to serve, well under the normal threshold for a change of overseas assignment.

"Are you guys as concerned as I am?" Bob asked. "Less than one year to serve may not mean anything. The army could extend your service and then send you there."

"The odds are on our side. Every day that goes by, our odds improve," Arnie said. "They could also choose to step up the draft and get additional recruits that way."

"We are worrying about nothing. General Westmoreland said it is now under control," Frank pointed out, and they all agreed they were safe for the moment.

"Forget all that," Rich said. "We are here to enjoy Paris. Let's look at the magnificent buildings and the beautiful women walking by."

They all laughed and finished their coffees.

Bob signaled the waiter. "L'addition, s'il vous plaît, par le tout." He'd asked for one check for the four of them. It came quickly. The waiter seemed eager to reuse the table with the great view. They paid the bill, left, and continued walking. Through the Latin Quarter and on to Île de la Cité.

The buildings were incredibly beautiful. They all wanted to see Notre-Dame. They passed by St. Chapel and then the Conciergerie. Under construction, Notre-Dame de

Paris was circled with scaffolding, but you could still go in. They walked to the roof and looked out over the city.

"Wow! A magnificent 360-degree view," Frank said.

There were gargoyles at the edge of the roof, looking out over the city as if to protect the residents from evil spirits.

Rich was also stunned by the great view. "Look there in the north. What is that beautiful white building?"

They looked it up. It was the Sacré-Cœur Basilica, high on a hill overlooking Montmartre, the artist quarter. The church dominated the view of the northern part of the city. It looked so magnificent, they decided to go there next.

Vowing to return to Île de la Cité the next day, they took the metro to Montmartre on the right bank, located within walking distance from their hotel. They all thought Paris was spectacular. Everyplace they went, they vowed to return to.

They walked up the hill at Montmartre, a mecca for artists and poets since the late 19th century. Even in December, the streets were crowded with tourists. They stopped in a small square to take photos. The Sacré-Cœur church was already in view. At the top of the hill, it could be seen for miles around.

The square had cobblestone streets and leafy trees in the center island, which also had many original paintings for sale. Away from the center were cafés with chairs outside, even in December. The cafés had red awnings and multicolored umbrellas to keep out the sun. A couple of artists were at their easels on the street. They would paint your portrait in ten minutes. As they walked up the hill to the church, the four musketeers saw other streets and squares also filled with tourists. An impressive sight for December.

They arrived at the Basilica of the Sacré-Cœur, according to many, one of the most beautiful and imposing structures in Paris. They took the required tourist photographs and went inside. They saw the Mosaic of Christ in Glory, and the bronze doors in the portico entrance illustrating scenes from Christ's life.

After wandering around the church for a while, they went back down to one of the squares and had sandwiches and coffee in a café there. The conversation again turned to what they would do when they got home.

"I spoke with my brother in Jacksonville again recently," Arnie said. "He is eager for me to get there. He believes my army experience will give me an edge in the insurance underwriting business."

"That's great, Arnie. I guess you can't really be sure of anything, but nothing ventured, nothing gained," Frank said. "It's the same for me. I am psyched up about returning to Los Angeles. I spoke with my uncle in Los Angeles again. He is expecting me to work with him at the Chevy dealership. He says he can't handle the workload alone anymore."

"I'm excited about the newspaper business," Rich said. "I haven't reached out yet, but I was the editor of my college newspaper and I hope that will give me an advantage."

Bob was unnerved by their certainty. "It sounds great that you all already know where you'll start. I was an economics major, but I don't have any contacts or family in business. My first mission when I get back will be to move out of the Bronx and into Manhattan. I'll figure things out from there. It's good to know that I'll have three successful friends to call on if I need help."

They all laughed, then paid the bill and walked back to the hotel.

The hotel concierge suggested some more places for them to visit the next day. First was Les Halles, the huge food market on the right bank, not far from Île de la Cité. The concierge said to get there early in the morning when you could see the market stalls being set up.

He also suggested typical tourist attractions like the Eiffel Tower and the Arc de Triomphe. They saw the challenge right away. Too many sights and too little time.

Hardly rested at the hotel, but showered and changed, they went back to the downtown area. There was a little market near their hotel, and they bought sandwiches and water and ate on the way. They went up the Eiffel Tower at night to see the view and take pictures. Paris was known as the city of light, and they could see why. Dazzling lights were all over downtown. The tower itself was lit up. They took some wonderful photos of the city at night. Across from the Eiffel Tower, there were fountains all bathed in light. Even the fountains near the tower were all aglow. Bob took a silhouetted profile photo of Rich with the lit-up fountains behind him.

They went back to the right bank and took some pictures on the Champs-Élysées. The Arc de Triomphe was bathed in yellow light. They stopped for coffee at an outdoor café facing the arch. The Champs-Élysées, crowded with traffic, had four lanes in each direction. Bob, obsessed with picture taking, rushed out to the small center island in the midst of it all and took some photos of the arch covered in yellow light.

Finally, when they had satisfied their desire to see Paris at night, they headed back to the hotel.

On Sunday morning, they got up bright and early. They walked over to Les Halles to see the market area early in the morning as the city came to life. None of them had seen such a huge market, and they were all amazed as they walked around. The daily market setup was already in progress, and trucks were arriving with all kinds of fruits, vegetables, meat, and fish.

They found a café with a perfect view of it all and ordered double espressos and croissants. Rich and Arnie stayed with regular coffee. Bob got adventurous and ordered a cerise, a cherry fruit tart. That became his go-to breakfast whenever he was in France.

The meat stall was nearby, and the fish market too. Cuts of meat of all sizes and shapes were hung on hooks and placed on tables. A lot of the stalls were outdoors, and they had small square zinc umbrellas to protect the wares from the sun.

There were a huge number of fish stalls. There were tables filled with ice and fish of all kinds, and even water tanks so the fish could be bought while alive.

A huge sign overhead read *Grande Kermesse du Poisson*.

It was a fish festival every day. *La fraicheur de la marée en vente ici*, another sign declared. The freshest of the sea sold here.

The city's main food market for hundreds of years, Les Halles was dismantled in 1971. No longer suited to modern city commerce, it would also have needed massive repairs. The market was then relocated to the suburb of Rungis.

They left the market and decided to go on a walking tour. They walked over the Pont au Change to the Île de la Cité and crossed the Île on the Boulevard du Palais, passing by the Conciergerie and St. Chapel. On the left bank, they walked through Saint-Germain-des-Prés in the direction of the Eiffel Tower. They stopped at a market on Rue De Buci, a small but crowded commercial street, and bought some sandwiches and drinks that they ate in a nearby park. They then continued walking past the Rodin museum, Les Invalides, and eventually arrived at the tower.

After taking a bunch more photos of the tower and the surroundings, they headed back to the hotel.

Tired but unbowed, they relaxed at the hotel for a while, then ventured out for a meal at a nearby pizzeria. It seemed that French people liked Italian food as there were many Italian restaurants and pizzerias.

After eating, they walked until they could walk no more, then returned to their hotel for the night.

In the morning, they checked out in time to make the 9:30 am train from Gare de l'Est for the trip back to Heidelberg. The four hopped into the second-class compartment. They were exhausted but happy about what they had seen and done. The train ride during the day made it hard to doze off, so they chatted and enjoyed the countryside passing by. They talked about the monuments, the French language, the food, the espresso coffee. None of the four were art lovers, so there was ample room for improvement.

It was their first time in Paris, and they had only seen the main sights. They were twenty-four years old and had spent only two and a half days there, so what could you expect?

Bob was very happy with how the trip had turned out. Not only had he enjoyed speaking French, but he liked the French too. They had taken pity on his attempts to speak their language and reached out to help. In less than 72 hours, they had seen the monuments, taken a tour on the

Seine, eaten at several French restaurants, seen Montmartre, Île de la Cité, and the Latin Quarter, and taken many wonderful photos. Wow!

Realizing how much he enjoyed Paris and how easy the trip was, Bob knew he would return there.

It would be only on those later trips that Bob would start to develop an appreciation for art. He would take the time to venture inside to see the great works of art at the Rodin museum, Louvre, Musée d'Orsay, and many other museums.

The chatter died down after a while, and they each seemed to be engaged in their own thoughts. The train barreled through the Saar valley and back into Germany. The farmland was always interesting to watch, and day travel allowed them to watch the land go by.

Later, they again chatted about how successful the trip was, and how well they all got along with one another. They agreed to plan a seven-day trip, which would be a little more complicated. They would use some leave days. Anything above seventy-two hours was considered leave, and they were entitled to only a certain number of leave days per year. Normally, you would want to save them for an emergency, but because they'd had such a great time together in Paris, they decided to try it. The question was where to go?

They were already in the dead of winter, so no nearby places would be fun. Traveling too far, on the other hand, would take up too much of the seven days.

In the summer, someone had suggested Switzerland, and they all came around to agree to plan a seven-day trip to Switzerland. It was far but easy to get to. It would also be a good place to visit in winter. It had everything they wanted, so they agreed to plan a trip to Switzerland for February. That would give them one month to plan it, get the leave approved, and get their work in order.

Late Monday afternoon, the weary foursome arrived back in Heidelberg, exhausted but happy. They grabbed a quick bite at the Enlisted Men's club and turned in for the night.

Bob lay on his bed with visions of travel in his head, unable to get to sleep. He thought about the huge fish market at Les Halles, and it took him back to his youth in the Bronx.

**Warner's Fish Market**

At about the age of twelve or thirteen, Bob had worked for a while at his uncle Warner's fish store. Warner's Fish Market was an institution on 170th Street. People came from afar to shop there. Located just a few blocks from where he lived, the store was easy for Bob to get to after school.

Seeing the Les Halles fish market being set up early in the morning reminded Bob that Uncle Warner would leave the house at 2 am every morning and drive his beautiful, red slatted truck down to the Fulton Street fish market in lower Manhattan to buy fresh fish to sell that day. Warner was steadfast. He ran the business for almost 40 years, providing a good lifestyle for Yolande, Pam, and Dave, as well as a great service for the neighborhood.

Bob worked one or two afternoons a week. His job was to deliver the fish orders to the ladies of the neighborhood. They would shop for fresh fish late in the morning, and their fish would be delivered in the afternoon.

Bob dragged a two-wheeled metal shopping cart that could hold many orders up the stairs of the five-story buildings that were common in the neighborhood. If he delivered ten orders, he could earn $10 in tips plus the $5 that Warner gave him, totaling $15 for a couple of hours of work. For a while, Bob earned his spending money that way.

The ladies enjoyed talking to Warner as much as buying the fish. He was an expert, and he was able to steer them right every time.

"No, you need two pounds of that."

"No, carp is the best fish to use for that dish."

"Here, I have a beautiful piece right here."

"Just bake it; it will be great."

They loved this back and forth, and they trusted him totally.

The week before Passover was on a whole different level. The neighborhood went fish crazy. Everyone wanted to serve fish. The store was packed from the time it opened until it closed. The store became a real family affair. Warner needed Yolande, Dave, and Pam to help out. It was a mob scene. Bob got there earlier too. He delivered more orders that week than in any other month.

The store had a narrow rectangular shape. On entering, the aisle to the right was to walk through. The cash register was on the left. During Passover, Pam was there, handling the register. She would also sell the shrimp and flounder fillets that were located on a table near the register. Next to that were the gleaming, ice-packed metal tables. They held all kinds of fish, some whole, some already cut into steaks, some filleted. Yolande was there, grinding fish and also selling.

Next was the work table that Warner used to cut and package the fish people would take along. Finally, there was a large metal fish tank filled with water and live fish. For some types of fish like carp, it was better for them to be freshly killed.

Dave had several important jobs. First of all, he accompanied Warner to the Fulton Fish Market in the early morning. By 6 am, he was tired before the day had even begun. At the store, he had to thaw out the "stiffs." These were the frozen fish that were to be sold that day. Then, he had to entertain the customers, who were almost all ladies of the neighborhood. They would have to wait in a five-deep line, sometimes for hours, to get their fish for

Passover. Dave was charming and kept them happy while they waited. He went on to be super successful in business. Maybe his experience at the fish store helped him.

Warner would pull a carp from the tank. Bam! The fish was clubbed on the head with a mallet made out of an old bowling pin. Warner then filleted the fish in an instant, and it was packaged and ready to go! It was a mob scene of activity that provided fresh fish for Passover for countless South Bronx families.

In his bed at Campbell Barracks, Bob realized that the further he went from the Bronx, the more he would be brought back to his Bronx memories. He slowly drifted to sleep with a smile on his face.

**Heidelberg in Winter**

December dragged on, and Heidelberg was enveloped in winter. The town was quiet. Late in December, Bob's driver's license was restored, but there was no place to go. So he did the same thing as before. He visited the car every few days and ran the engine. Now that he had his license back, he also took it out on the Autobahn if there was no snow, putting some miles on it to keep the engine tuned.

New Year's Eve was approaching, and thoughts of that offered a joyful escape from the winter. Fats and His Cats were performing on New Year's Eve, and the whole crowd was going to be there. Even the married couples.

Bob traveled downtown from time to time when it didn't snow. The town was always quiet as he walked along the river. There was an eerie whiteness and few people on the streets. Philosopher's Walk on the hill overlooking the town was deserted but beautiful.

A bowling league got started. There were several experienced bowlers, and it was a great way to pass the cold, winter days. Bob had bowled in the Bronx, so he was no stranger to it. The league was organized into eight teams of four, and the bowling matches took place on Tuesday evenings and Sunday mornings.

There were snowball fights, which Bob loved; they reminded him of the Bronx.

New Year's Eve came. Their little group needed two tables at the club. There were about sixteen people including the married couples.

The four travelers – Frank, Rich, Arnie, and Bob – wisely got there early as tables couldn't be reserved. They started a bridge game and ordered some beers and fries.

Talk turned to their recent trip to Paris. Remembering how well they had gotten along together, they talked again about the longer trip to Switzerland.

"I planned out a ten-day trip to Switzerland for us. If you like it, we can start to firm up the plans," Arnie announced.

"Lucky the trip to Paris went so well. Otherwise, there is no way we could commit to such a long trip," Rich commented.

"Arnie, are you saying I'll have to room with you again, but this time for ten days? Aargh!" Bob joked.

They all laughed, and then agreed to ten days, knowing that long a time would maximize the payback for all that time on a train.

Arnie described his plans for the trip. "We'll take the overnight train to Geneva and spend two nights there. Then we'll work our way east with two nights in Lucerne, one night in Zurich, and three nights in Salzburg, Austria. Then finally, an overnight train back to Heidelberg. A distance of 1,400 miles in ten days, all courtesy of the European railroad system. How does that sound?"

Rich, Frank, and Bob were awed. "Sounds great," they said in unison. They applauded, and Arnie smiled and bowed. The trip was set.

At around 5 pm, more people started arriving, and a couple of them saved the adjoining table, where the married couples and a few other latecomers would sit. Finally, the bridge game ended, and they focused on the conversation as they all caught up.

After a while, they ordered dinner. Bob, happy he wasn't waiting, ordered the usual cheeseburger and fries. After seeing all those slim Parisians, he thought he might have to soon change his diet, but not that night.

Fats and His Cats came out for their first set. The stage was festive with banners and balloons. The waiters distributed hats and horns to the guests at the tables.

The band played several holiday songs, saving "Auld Lang Syne" for midnight. They played the popular stuff, including a song that had been popular all year, "San Francisco." It perfectly captured the restless youth movement going on at the time.

Then they sang a song that had come out in November, "I am the Walrus," from the Beatles film, *Magical Mystery Tour*. The audience loved that one. Ironically, with all the youth unrest and the U.S. and Vietnamese soldiers dying in Vietnam, the BBC chose to ban the song shortly after its release because they didn't approve of part of the song.

Finally, midnight came and toasts were made. It was an extraordinary moment. This special group of friends from all over America, thrown together by circumstance, were celebrating the only New Year's Eve they would ever spend together.

1968 had arrived, but January dragged. Winter continued its grip on Heidelberg. The town was a gray and white ghost, especially during snow flurries.

On weekends, they still walked downtown. There were far fewer people than in summer. On one trip, Bob and the others bought heavy boots for the trip to Switzerland.

They threw themselves into the bowling league and bridge at the Enlisted Men's club in the evenings to pass the time.

In mid-January, they noticed a change in Charlie. He was not as quick to smile or laugh. He was quiet and was keeping to himself more. Drinking more than usual too. At first, they thought it was the winter doldrums, but after a week or so they decided on an intervention. One evening at the club, Bob, Frank, and Rich confronted him.

"Charlie, come on now. What gives?" Bob asked him. "You've been moping around for a week. It can't be our company. We are such upbeat guys and great conversationalists. Is everything OK at home?"

Charlie finally relented. He knew he couldn't fool them for long. "Linda broke up with me last week," he said.

"What happened?" Bob asked. "Everything was going great."

"She told me she doesn't see a future for us. That, long-term, my career wouldn't be sufficient for the lifestyle she wants. That all the other factors don't make up for it."

"That's crazy," Frank said. "How can she even know how successful you will be? Is there another guy?"

"She wouldn't say, so there probably is," Charlie said. "I've been down in the dumps since that phone call."

"Charlie, we are very sorry to hear this," Rich said. "You should mourn for a while over this loss, but just keep in mind you are young, single, and not horrible looking." That got a smile from him. "When you get back home, the girls will be throwing themselves at you," Rich went on.

"Yes, I know. It's just that I'm feeling pretty bad right now."

"You know what you ought to do is visit Amsterdam again," Arnie said. "This time, we'll all go along and have a great time together."

Charlie brightened a little, seeing he wasn't alone. They ordered another round of beers and drank some toasts to visiting Amsterdam. Then they changed the subject. They learned that the winter festival of Fasching would start soon, toward the end of February.

"I have read that anything goes during Fasching," Bob said. "So, in only a few weeks we'll be having a fantastic time right here, and spring will be right behind it."

"Charlie, why don't you come to Switzerland with us next month? It would do you good," Arnie said.

"I don't think so," Charlie said. "I'm in no mood for that. I would just bring you guys down. No, I'm better off just wallowing in my grief for a while. Maybe I'll go to Amsterdam alone one time. We'll see."

So, they left it at that.

**Tet**

Then came January 30, 1968, and with it the North Vietnamese Tet offensive that changed everything they thought they knew about the war in Vietnam.

The Tet offensive was a campaign of surprise attacks against South Vietnamese and U.S. forces during the Lunar New Year holiday.

More than 80,000 North Vietnamese Army and Viet Cong soldiers attacked more than 100 towns and cities including thirty-six of the forty-four provincial capitals in the largest military operation conducted by either side up to that point in the war. It was breathtaking in scope.

The attacks were stunning in the degree of their coordination and their widespread geographic footprint. No one thought that an attack of that size and scope could even be contemplated by the North Vietnamese, let alone carried out.

While there were rumblings of enemy action beforehand, one U.S. military intelligence analyst said, "If we'd gotten the whole battle plan, it wouldn't have been believed. It wouldn't have been credible to us."

The U.S. and South Vietnam forces were surprised and lost control of several important cities temporarily. Although they regrouped and counterattacked, inflicting heavy casualties on the North Vietnamese and VC, the political damage was done.

Although, in a sense, Tet was a military defeat for the North Vietnamese (50,000 dead, all the cities retaken), it was, for them, a huge political victory that changed everything. American public opinion supporting the war declined quickly afterward.

Having told President Johnson and the American public that things were in hand only two months before, General Westmoreland now reported that defeating North Vietnam would require an additional 200,000 troops. After a one-year decline, the U.S. draft started increasing again. In 1968, over 68,000 more civilians than in 1967 were drafted, a 29% increase at a time when the war was supposed to be winding down.

In Heidelberg, the news hit like an electric shock. Just like the American public, Bob and his friends had believed everything was in hand. Unlike the American public, they knew their service could be extended and they could be sent to Vietnam the next day.

A pall was cast over the command in Heidelberg. People in Bob's circle had always felt they were helping the war effort by keeping Europe running. Now they saw that wasn't enough, not nearly enough. They wondered if they would have to give more.

Among Bob and his friends, the discussions of their plans took on a little less certainty and joy. They began to increase the diversions and travel and live even more for the moment as they wondered what lay ahead for them.

# Chapter Seven – Switzerland, February '68

Everyone was ready to forget about Vietnam and the gray winter in Heidelberg. The opportunity to do so soon came. Bob, Frank, Arnie, and Rich had planned their trip to Switzerland and were leaving the next week. The night before departure, they met in the Enlisted Men's club.

Bob had been changing his diet to include salads, and some of the other guys had followed suit, but it was impossible to eliminate the cheeseburgers and fries just yet. They could smell the food arriving at the tables nearby. Aah! The smell of the fries was as irresistible as the taste. After an hour at the club, Bob's mouth was watering for that taste. They all ordered the burgers and fries.

The band was playing the latest music. Aretha Franklin's "Chain of Fools" had just hit number one in the charts. She was a big favorite in Heidelberg. That was followed by the Temptations' "I Wish it Would Rain." The Beatles and the Rolling Stones were the music royalty. All the bands played their songs.

They finalized the plan. Charlie would drive them to the train station. Everyone had their work in order. Bob's Line of Duty investigations had progressed satisfactorily. All was ready for departure.

They went over the checklist. Warm clothes, long johns, the boots they had all recently bought. Each of them had converted several hundred U.S. dollars into Deutschmarks and Swiss francs the previous week.

On departure night, all went according to plan. Charlie dropped them off, and they bought tickets at the station and waited on the platform, with one bag each. Bob was wearing his green, quilted ski jacket that now had two patches, including the recent addition for Paris.

It was dark. Thanks to street lamp-type lighting, though, the station was well lit. But it smelled of diesel.

"Aah, I love the smell of diesel," Arnie said, sharing his dry humor. "It means we are traveling."

The overnight train to Geneva arrived on time, and they climbed aboard.

The train was long, and the locomotive had a streamlined look, reminding them of the trains they had taken to Paris and Amsterdam.

The shrill whistle was like music, marking the beginning of this next adventure.

Second class was first class to them. They were happy to travel in economy class so they could afford the experience. Others, not in their strategic European location, could not even hope to do so.

They settled in for the 300-mile trip to Geneva and chatted for a while about Vietnam, about home, and about how lucky they were to be on this trip without a care in the world.

The clackety, clackety-clack of the train kept them awake a while longer and occasionally woke them during the night.

Bob awoke at 2 am to the sound of Frank snoring like crazy. A poke in the ribs woke him momentarily, and the snoring eased when he settled back.

They arrived in Geneva at around 4:30 am and left the station. The wind coming off Lake Geneva hit them like a brick wall. It was cold, in the thirties. Unlike Heidelberg, Geneva was high – 1,225 feet above sea level.

About three streets from the Cornavin station, they found a cheap hotel. It was a narrow building with a small, creaky elevator. They settled in and were ready to see the sights by 9 am. It was a cold, gray day, but not snowing. They walked down to the lake. The city looked low rise and had a mix of functional, rectangular-shaped buildings and beautiful domed ones. Along the lake, there were some coin-operated telescopes. Rich grabbed one, put in a coin, and looked at the lake and part of the city.

"Whatever happened to sharing?" Bob asked.

Rich smiled and offered the telescope to Bob for a moment.

They all took turns and saw some glimpses of the lake and the town.

The main tourist seasons in Switzerland are summer and the winter ski season. February is the height of the ski season. So while they were there, the mountain resorts were all crowded and the cities empty. Walking around, they saw hardly anyone. But they were in a major European city and loved it.

Switzerland is a smallish country, about half the size of South Carolina, sandwiched between France and Germany, with Italy to the south. Each Swiss region is heavily influenced by its neighbors. Geneva is in the southwest of the country, shaped like a finger sticking into the heart of eastern France. The official language of Geneva is French. Bob was thrilled that he could continue to stumble along in that language and still be the spokesperson for the group.

Geneva is a functional city. Not as beautiful as Paris or as open and engaging as Amsterdam. It is an international city of finance and diplomacy with many agencies of the United Nations there, as well as the headquarters of the International Red Cross.

They walked around downtown, stopped for lunch, then continued walking.

They had heard that Switzerland, and Geneva in particular, was known for its chocolate. They stopped in a chocolate shop and were taken aback. The sight and smell of the chocolate flooded their senses. It was a rich, heavy aroma, that you almost had to swim through. They stood there for a while, transfixed, in an other-worldly state.

Encouraged by the shopkeeper to try the samples, they indulged, trying chocolates of different kinds. Bob liked the bittersweet the most. On the shelf were displays of what looked like kettles of chocolate wrapped in foil.

The shopkeeper, speaking English, explained they were "cauldrons" that commemorated the defeat of an attack on Geneva in 1602 by troops sent by Charles, Emmanuel I, Duke of Savoy. The cauldrons were used to drop hot oil onto the invaders and defeat them.

The shopkeeper had a passion to share what he knew. "In 1819, Francois Louis Cailler created the first chocolate factory in Geneva. The invention of milk chocolate came in 1875. Notice how the best quality chocolate breaks cleanly. No crumbs. To decide which one you like best, you must try many kinds. A not-so-awful task."

"It is very kind of you to share this history of chocolate with us," Frank said to the shopkeeper.

"Not at all. It is my pleasure. In the winter, fewer people pass by the shop. Also, I have learned these facts over thirty years in this business. They are crowded into my brain. Sometimes it feels like my head will explode if I do not let them out."

After buying several packages of chocolate, they left the shop and continued on their way. They walked all over the old town and down to the banks of the Rhone, where there were many elegant hotels and restaurants.

Finally, they returned to their hotel. After showering and relaxing for a while, they went out to dinner and on to a local bar recommended by the concierge. It was cold in the evening. They had all put on shirts with sweaters on top and were wearing their heaviest jackets.

The bar, which was near the hotel, was small and crowded. It was the most people they had seen all day. The bar was narrow and dark, nicely painted and decorated, with large paintings on the wall in the back. Some small tables on the side faced the heavy wooden bar, and there was a huge number of liquor bottles on shelves behind the bar. Most of the patrons were well dressed and looked as if they had just come from work. The most beautiful part was the bartender. She was about 22 years old, with dark hair and a beautiful smile that lit up the place. The four musketeers all fell in love instantly. Bob felt lucky because, speaking some French, he fantasized that he had the best chance with her.

But he felt scared too. *What if I blow it?* he thought. As if he had any real chance.

They spent a couple of hours there, speaking with the people near them who spoke English. They drank brandy from a gigantic green glass brandy snifter that could have held a gallon. The bartender said it was a tradition. Bob spent most of the two hours talking with the bartender in French. He realized that he had nothing to lose but everything to gain. If she shot him down, his buddies would not even know what was said. But she did not. She was charming throughout. Just not interested in Bob.

On the way out, Bob muttered, "I couldn't figure it out. Here I am, an amazing catch. A U.S. Army soldier with no idea how he will earn a living later, but already earning $250 per month."

They all broke up laughing as they walked over to the taxi stand at the corner. The taxi dropped them back at the hotel, and they collapsed into bed.

The next day would be another walk-around day.

Bob was always the early riser of any group and that day was no exception. Up at around 4:30 am, he threw on his pants with long johns underneath, a sweater, and his green ski jacket, then headed out. He walked around the old town, getting his bearings and grabbing a coffee at a local coffee shop. He had a restless energy and needed to be overprepared for everything. Finally, he returned to the room at around 7 am to find the others just waking up. They all went out to a local cafeteria-type restaurant for a breakfast of rolls, toast, jam, cheese, and coffee.

In the old town, they walked over to the University of Geneva to see the Reformation Wall. The wall contains a series of imposing sculptures that were created to honor the Protestant Reformation. It was unveiled in 1909 to commemorate the 400th anniversary of John Calvin's birth. Calvin had founded the University of Geneva.

Then they visited the nearby St. Pierre cathedral, which dominated a section of the old town. It was built as a Roman Catholic church but became a Protestant church during the Reformation. John Calvin gave his sermons there in the mid-16th century. It was a beautifully detailed Gothic-style church with a commanding view of the lake.

Walking back toward the lake, they stopped at a couple of swanky jewelry stores on the Rue du Rhone, right where Lake Geneva flows into the Rhone. One of the elegant shopping streets of the city, the Rue du Rhone was home to many of the fine watch showrooms in Geneva. Frank, who wanted to become wealthy, tried on a couple of Rolex watches. The prices were way beyond what he could afford, but as he said, "You can dream."

Bob guessed that the perfectly crafted watches, as well as the perfectly crafted chocolates, were the creative expression of a country of limited land area. It seemed as if they needed to create small jewels because of the country's limited space.

They turned in early, after a long day of walking and seeing the city, and checked out the next morning. They walked to the train station and boarded the train for the next leg of the trip. They were heading to Lucerne, in the central part of the country.

It was another bright and sunny day. The scenery was breathtaking. Snowcapped mountains and lakes everywhere. There was little conversation. All four pairs of eyes were riveted on the white, snowcapped mountain peaks slowly passing in the distance. The sky was a crisp blue, and the trees whizzed by in the foreground. None of them had seen anything like this before. It was like traveling through a Kodachrome slide.

The most interesting part of the trip was the change in language. As the miles passed and people got on and off the train, the passengers were suddenly speaking a different language, a sort of lilting combination of French and German. They later learned it was called Schwiizerdütsch. Days later, during the trip to Zurich and Salzburg, the spoken language changed to all German. It was fascinating that the language changed so dramatically to reflect the local culture in such a short distance.

Arnie had booked two rooms at an inn just outside of Lucerne on the way to Mount Pilatus. Lucerne is a charming town on Lake Lucerne in central Switzerland. All around are mountain views. It is situated just north of Mount Pilatus, which at 7,000 feet, towers above the lake and town. The Mount Pilatus mountain top was one of the must-see places on the trip.

A taxi from the train station took them to the inn. There was snow everywhere, but the roads were clear and dry. The sky was blue with a few cotton ball clouds. In short, it was a picture-perfect alpine day.

But it was not to last. The innkeeper showed them to their rooms and let them know that a storm was on the way, and would hit that night or the next morning. They quickly stowed their bags. Bob and Arnie were still rooming together. Frank and Rich took the other room. Determined to enjoy the nice weather, they walked north to the Reuss River and then down to the lake.

They crossed Chapel Bridge into the old town. The 600-foot-long covered wooden bridge was built in the 14th century and is the town's emblem. They walked around the narrow winding streets of Sternenplatz. At Restaurant Fritschi, they saw some amazing painted murals depicting ogres and other Mardi Gras characters.

They knew they had arrived too early for the Fastnacht celebration, but they would be back in Heidelberg in time for the pre-Lenten Fasching celebration. They crossed back to the southern bank and finally took a taxi back to the inn.

In the afternoon the sky darkened and, ominously, the wind died.

**Ice Skating**

Not wanting to venture far from the inn, they found a covered ice-skating rink nearby. Rich, who was from the Midwest, was an avid skater and suggested they try it. They entered the huge building, which was open at the sides but covered on top. They rented skates and changed on some benches.

The only one of the four who could skate was Rich. Not Arnie from Dallas, not Frank from Los Angeles, and certainly not Bob from the South Bronx. Rich gave them a group lesson and then went on his way. He looked professional and even skated backward a couple of times.

Bob experienced another sport he had somehow missed in his youth, but he had no desire to embrace this one.

Bob, Frank, and Arnie stumbled along but couldn't turn, and could not even stop except by crashing into a wall. Bob mastered the butt slide as his way of stopping. After an hour or so, they had enough, changed back into their boots, and returned the gear. A fun afternoon.

That night, the storm struck. High winds and large snowflakes pelted the town. They decided to stay at the inn and have dinner there.

The dining room was warmly lit. A fire burning in the large fireplace on one side of the room warmed them as they sat at a nearby table. The French language, having gone missing on the train to Lucerne, was no help to them there. Luckily, the waitress spoke some English.

Fondue was prominent on the menu, but none of them knew what it was.

The waitress explained. "Fondue is a very popular wintertime dish. It's several cheeses that are served in a hot pot with pieces of bread. It really warms you up."

So, they gave the fondue a try.

According to the menu, it was *Kaasfondue*. It consisted of Emmenthaler and Gruyere cheese melted in a pot with white wine, garlic, and nutmeg. It came with a large bread, broken into smaller pieces, and long forks to use to dip the bread into the melted cheese.

It only sounded strange until you tasted it. They soon realized that it was delicious, and truly a communal dinner. You just had to avoid dropping the bread into the pot of cheese. Doing so was considered bad manners.

Now in the German part of Switzerland, Bob saw that Hofbräu beer was on tap. Remembering the great Hofbräu beer at Oktoberfest, he ordered one, and the others followed suit.

They talked first about the day.

"Where did you learn to skate like that, Rich?" Bob asked.

"You can't grow up in the Midwest without learning to ice skate or without rooting for the Chicago Blackhawks. My dad took me to plenty of games over the years. Naturally, when I wasn't there this past year, they had their best season ever," Rich lamented. "They finished in first place for the first time in the history of the franchise. Of course, they were then beaten in the best-of-seven NHL playoffs in only six games, but so what?"

"Wow! We had nothing like that where I'm from in Dallas," Arnie said.

After a couple of hours, they had polished off the fondue and a few beers. They followed that with 140-proof cinnamon schnapps for extra warmth.

The conversation turned to the next day. They had to decide whether to go to Mount Pilatus or not. On the one hand, the weather would be horrible, but on the other, they could not hang around for another day waiting for the weather to clear.

They agreed they would decide in the morning. And because of the bad weather, the vote to go up the mountain would have to be unanimous. Any one of them could veto the trip. The snow was still coming down as they retired to their rooms after a full, satisfying day.

**Mount Pilatus**

In the morning, the snow had stopped, but the clouds remained and the sky was dark. The forecast was for more snow.

In the inn's dining room, their table was set with rolls and a pot of steaming hot coffee. The waitress brought out small jars of different flavored jams, and triangle-shaped cheeses packaged in tinfoil. At the buffet, there was muesli, along with yogurt and fruit. Outside, the sky was still dark. They felt no need to rush through breakfast.

They had been counting on going to Mount Pilatus. The concierge, however, strongly urged them to wait until the next day when the weather was supposed to clear. But they had to leave the next morning.

They debated what to do. Bob and Rich leaned toward not going. The sky was dark and ominous, it could snow again, and who knew what the mountain top would look like. Frank, though, wanted to push on and take the chance.

"When the heck will we ever get this chance again?" he said.

Arnie, always the voice of reason, agreed with Frank. "We are young now, with no wives or children to worry about. We should take the chance. What's the worst that could happen? You go up in a cable car. They are professionals. The operator won't go up if it is too dangerous. The law of averages is way in our favor."

Slowly, Bob and Rich came around, and after a third cup of coffee, it was unanimous. It was a go.

Dressed in their warmest clothing, including long johns, they took a taxi to the base of the mountain. It was cold, and the sky was still threatening, but there was no snow yet. The cable car was operating.

"There is no visibility today," said the ticket seller. "You can go up, but the weather might force us to close. Then you would have to come right back down, and we couldn't refund your money."

Along with several others, they went up in the cable car.

As they rose, the mist got thicker and the wind got stronger. The cable car made a metallic creaking noise as it swayed from side to side in the wind at first and then settled down. A mist clung to the windows. Visibility was zero.

The wind suddenly gusted. The car swayed some more and settled down again in its slow ascent. The passengers' faces tensed, but the operator's face was calm.

"This is perfectly normal for a day like this. We'll be there soon," the operator said.

Finally, the car steadied and traveled smoothly the rest of the way.

It was cold. It was very cold. Their long johns and ski jackets only warmed them a little.

Bob shivered. "I can't believe this. This is the coldest I have ever been."

The others nodded while shivering too.

When the car slipped under the building, there was a communal sigh of relief. The passengers stepped through the car's open door and walked into the aerie's hospitality center, which contained a lounge, a restaurant, and a snack bar.

No one was there but the few employees working the snack bar. The information desk was deserted, but the snack bar was serving food. They ordered hot soup and sandwiches and looked out the picture windows in disbelief. Nothing!

A thick white mist pelted the windows and dribbled down them. Outside the windows was a phantasmagoric scene of white haze and mist everywhere. Only dark stripes showed where the sides of the mountain were.

The doors to the outside terrace were locked. Security would not allow anyone outside until the conditions improved.

"We can't afford to lose even one tourist," the guard said, smiling.

They enjoyed their hot onion and vegetable soup and melted cheese sandwiches. By the time they had finished, they were warm and took off their jackets. They finished the meal with strong coffee and pastries.

They took photographs but knew they were getting nothing. Bob went into the souvenir shop and bought a couple of professionally done Kodachrome slides of the view from Mount Pilatus. Along with the souvenir booklets of photos, that was all they were going to see of the normally fantastic view of the mountain tops in the distance, the town, and the lake 7,000 feet below.

After an hour or so, the weather had only worsened, and they were told to take the cable car back down. It had resumed snowing but was less windy. The cable car was steadier as they descended to the base of the mountain. They called a taxi, which arrived after 45 minutes and took them back to their hotel, where they remained for the evening.

At dinner, they toasted their survival on Mount Pilatus with Hofbräu beer.

"I am thrilled we decided to go," Bob said to the others. "Arnie, thanks for convincing us. Way to go."

Frank raised his glass. "We gambled and won. Here's to us"

The others hurrahed and drank the toast.

"Looking at these postcard photos, it is amazing how little we could see," Rich said.

"We saw nothing but experienced a hell of a lot," replied Arnie. "I am glad we are here in one piece."

They smiled and toasted the cable car.

"Here's to that cable car. I thought we were goners," Rich said. They all laughed.

After dinner, they called it a day and went to bed.

The whole purpose of the trip was to open new vistas and get their minds off Heidelberg and Vietnam. It was working beautifully.

Early the next morning, they headed to the train station for the trip to Salzburg, Austria, their furthest stop on the journey.

The trip to Salzburg was beautiful and uneventful. Great scenery again. And the mountains in the distance looked like postcards. It had stopped snowing and the sky was blue. The train trip was long and took most of the day. They talked about their time in Lucerne, the beautiful views, and how scared they had been riding the cable car to the top of Mount Pilatus.

**Salzburg**

They arrived at Salzburg late in the afternoon and settled in at their hotel.

"What do we know about Salzburg?" Frank asked.

Ever prepared, Bob pulled out the travel book and read. "It's one of the largest cities in Austria, situated in a level basin on both sides of the Salzach River near the northern foothills of the Alps. It was very wealthy at one point. Impressed by the opulence of Rome, they built the city in a similar Baroque architecture style, and it has been referred to as the Rome of the North."

"Don't you get tired of being prepared for everything?" Rich half-joked. "Why not live in the spur of the moment sometimes?"

"You're right, Rich. I do that too much. I just hate being surprised or delayed. I don't know why." Bob paused. "Should I continue?"

"Sure," they all said.

"The name Salzburg means salt castle, and its name comes from the barges carrying salt on the Salzach River. It is also the home of Mozart. We should walk around the old city, see the cathedral, and also see Mozart's birthplace. Then there is Mount Untersberg just outside the city for the next day if we are all brave enough to go to another mountain top."

They all agreed that it sounded great.

They unpacked, changed into slacks and sweaters, and headed down to the old town. Despite the winter weather, the old town was crowded. They walked around a bit and stopped in front of a small restaurant on Getreidegasse, the main shopping street. It was getting close to dinner time.

The restaurant was called the Central Café, and it looked crowded inside. After a brief wait, they were seated at a table for four. The meal was extraordinary. Wiener schnitzel, roasted potatoes, green beans. The Wiener schnitzel had a wonderful lemony aroma and was melt-in-your-mouth tender. Bob saw they had Hofbräu beer on tap, and ordered that. Two hours later, they finished the best meal of the trip and retired to the hotel. They decided to go to the Central Café again the next night.

As usual, Bob was up at 4:30 the next morning. He got dressed and left the room with Arnie still sleeping and walked all over downtown, returning at 7 with some coffee for Arnie.

"What's going on?" Arnie asked, the sleep still on his face.

"Just the usual," Bob said. "I went out for my walk. The old town is beautiful, and I love this time of day. Just before sunrise, the promise of the day is still unlimited. We should walk around the old town this morning. Then we can figure out the trip to the mountain for tomorrow. Here, I brought you some coffee."

Arnie drank a big sip of the coffee and started to wake up.

"Yeah, that sounds good."

Arnie got dressed. They woke up Frank and Rich by knocking on their door, then went down to the lobby to wait for them. Frank and Rich appeared fifteen minutes later. They went to a local café for breakfast, then continued their walking tour of the old town.

It was a perfect day, cold and crisp but sunny with blue skies.

They walked to the old town and over to the Domplatz, the site of the old cathedral. Founded in 774 on the remnants of a Roman town, the massive church was rebuilt in the seventeenth century as a Baroque cathedral of the Roman Catholic Archdiocese of Salzburg. Mozart was baptized there.

They entered the plaza through one of the three open arches. The building itself is constructed of a dark gray stone accented with Untersberg marble. The church property is on a bluff with a commanding view from the south side of the river.

They went inside and walked around the beautiful interior, took some photos, and left to resume their walk.

Being February, the town wasn't jam-packed, but there were a good number of tourists.

They continued to the river walk and saw the streets and the shops, finally walking along the main shopping street, the Getreidegasse. The narrow street provided a perfect showcase for all the things on offer. Advertising each business, signs in a variety of dazzling colors and shapes hung overhead. Colorful pendants were also hung, advertising some of the shops.

Next, they went to see Hohensalzburg Fortress, which sits atop the Festungsberg mountain at about 1,500 feet, looking down to the old town and the river. Reminded of Heidelberg Schloss, they rode the cable car up to the castle and walked around the broad balcony, enjoying the spectacular views below, then descended back to the town and continued the all-day march.

After lunch, they walked along Getreidegasse, stopping at number 9, Mozart's birthplace. Mozart was born in this house on January 27, 1756. He was the seventh child of Leopold Mozart, a musician of the Salzburg Royal Chamber. Today, Mozart is the town's local hero and top tourist attraction.

With some time to spare before dinner, and being very close to the Central Café, they visited all three floors. They were filled with almost everything about Mozart; life: portraits, documents, musical instruments.

Walking up and down the stairs put the final touches to their all-day walk. They were all starving by the time they got to the Central Café, two hours later.

They were seated right away, and immediately ordered beers and toasted their day's good fortune. Then the talk switched to the next day's visit to Mount Untersberg. Dinner came, and it was as delicious as the one the day before.

Afterward, bellies full and filled with good memories of the day, they went back to the hotel for an early turn-in. No one mentioned any concerns about the war or their immediate futures. They had finally arrived "in the moment."

Bob did not do his usual walk the next morning. Having seen the old town twice, he went out for a brief walk in the bitter cold early morning and then stopped for some coffee. That day was going to be the day for wearing every layer of clothing you had.

They took a taxi ten miles south of town to the base of Mount Untersberg. There, they bought tickets and boarded the cable car for the climb to the top at 6,400 feet.

They stepped outside. It was freezing cold but sunny, and the skies were clear. The mountain towered over the area and offered a stunning view of the valley below, just south of Salzburg.

Bundled up as much as possible, they took the snow-covered trail to the top. There, they gazed at the spectacular view of the mountains and the valley below. The steep slope was covered in snow, but some trees and grass were untouched by the snow. A couple of house roofs dotted the slope. 4,000 feet straight down, there were a couple of towns connected by roads and many little dots that were almost certainly houses.

They looked to the south and saw an amazing vista of snowcapped mountain peaks. Their view was filled with mountain peaks, white with snow and dark where there was no snow, with just a handful of long horizontal barrel-shaped clouds in the distance. They gazed at the scene for some time, then took pictures. There were no indications of where they were. They could have been at Mount Untersberg or they could have been at 8,000 meters in the Himalayas. They just could not tell.

After a while, they started the descent back to the station. That was when they noticed that the ice was slippery. There wasn't a solid railing to hold on to. There was just a single iron railing with one horizontal bar at about chest height. Further down, there was just a chest-high horizontal wire. If you lost your balance and slipped through it, your next stop was four thousand feet below.

They became a little tense as they carefully walked down, grateful for the boots they had bought in Heidelberg. At one point, Arnie decided to take off his boots because he thought his bare feet would give him better traction.

Finally inside the station, they warmed up with hot chocolate while they waited for the next cable car. They descended the mountain and took a taxi back to the hotel. Later, they took another walk around town, had another dinner at the Central Café, and turned in for the night.

The next morning, they caught the 10 am train to Heidelberg. The trip back was uneventful, except for the great scenery, which made them happy to be traveling during the day. They arrived back at Heidelberg after dark, took a taxi to the base, and turned in for the night.

Bob could not get to sleep. He lay on his bunk thinking how lucky he was and how far he had come from the Bronx. He shivered as he remembered how cold he had been at the top of Mount Pilatus.

The last time he had been that cold was years before. The memory of the cold brought to mind his crazy trip to Buffalo in February five or six years before.

**Buffalo**

One of his friends had a connection with a harness driver at Yonkers Raceway and had gotten a "hot" tip on a horse that was racing several days later at Batavia Downs, just outside of Buffalo, New York.

His friends asked Bob to go along on the seven-hour trip, and he agreed. With five of them in the roomy Pontiac le Mans driven by Mort, they started out from the Bronx in the early afternoon to bet on a horse in Buffalo, New York. They had no idea which of the nine races the horse was running in, or where the racetrack was, or how long it would take to get there. Let's just say this was not a precision, military-style operation.

Mort was handsome, with a full head of brown, curly hair. A bit older than Bob, he was an insurance claims adjuster. He always had a new car and a pretty girl on his arm.

They drove for nine hours, just stopping for gas and snacks. Pop music was playing on the radio. Bob remembered "Breaking Up Is Hard To Do" by Neil Sedaka and "Big Girls Don't Cry" and "Sherry" by the Four Seasons.

They were way late, arriving at Batavia Downs just as the eighth race got underway. Amazingly enough, the horse was running in the ninth and final race.

They were able to place their bets on him. After a nine-hour drive, and providence holding the horse for the final race, they all bet big. Bob bet the whole $50 he had brought along. After a great start, the horse naturally finished last, putting the idea of providence in a whole different light.

But that was when it started to get interesting. "We can't just go back like losers, without making the most of this. Let's do something while we're here," Mort said.

Steve, one of the other guys, chipped in. "You know Niagara Falls is right near here. Why don't we go there and see the falls?"

So, at 11 pm, on one of the coldest nights of February, these five geniuses drove to Niagara Falls, parked the car, and walked to the viewing area.

"It must be zero degrees," Bob said, his teeth chattering as the wind whipped into them from across the water. Everyone was shivering with cold. "I can't believe we are doing this. I have never been so cold in my life."

But, standing at the rail, at the side of the falls, freezing and shivering, they saw an amazing sight. Gigantic chunks of ice were barreling to the edge of the Niagara River and toppling over the falls to the frozen river below. The power, the noise, and the cold were all overwhelming.

CRACK, BOOM, CRACK, BOOM.

They looked down over the edge and saw the huge ice chunks hit the water with incredible force. They were mesmerized, but when they could stand the cold no longer, they got back in the car and headed back to New York City, the ill-fated trip to Buffalo over.

In his bunk at Campbell Barracks, Bob shivered again at the memories, but then slowly drifted to sleep.

**Fasching**

The next night, they went to the Enlisted Men's club for the evening. It was a good chance to relive the great trip and share the adventure. Charlie and a couple of the others were there too.

"Wow, I'm sorry I didn't go along," Charlie said. "Well, we still have six or seven months. I'll go on the next one."

"Great," said Frank. "I know someone who was stationed in Berlin. We should go there as soon as we can. West Berlin is a beautiful, hip city, and we should see it."

"That would be great," Arnie said. "I would like to see East Berlin, too. And go across at Checkpoint Charlie. I hear you can do that."

"Sounds like it's agreed. Berlin is next," Bob said.

"Count me in," Charlie said. "How could I not go through a checkpoint named after me?"

The show was getting started. It was a German rock band. They played the popular stuff and a lot of soul music. Wilson Pickett, James Brown. The dance floor got crowded. They finished with the Temptations' "I Wish it Would Rain." The dancers went into a slow dance and seemed to be in a trance. What a song!

Finally, they called it a night. On his bunk later, Bob thought about his last trip, the next one to Berlin, and what a lucky guy he was. The money from Yolande's loan was decreasing, but there was still some left. He knew he could never duplicate his experiences.

Their timing was perfect. Far from returning to a moribund, winter-bound Heidelberg, an explosion of life was about to happen. It was called Fasching. About two weeks before Lent, in the middle of winter, Heidelberg briefly came out of hibernation and sprang back to life.

The streets were crowded, day and night. The restaurants and wine cellars were filled with people. In the pre-Lenten period between Epiphany and Ash Wednesday, the saying was "anything goes." Alcohol was also forbidden during Lent, so everyone was drinking now.

Bob and his buddies at the office were due to leave Heidelberg in September, only seven months later, when their term of service was up. For them, Fasching began a frenetic spring and summer of "getting it all in" before their departure in the fall.

The Fasching festival culminated in a wild parade on Fat Tuesday, February 27, the day before Ash Wednesday. Bob, Charlie, and Frank took a day's leave just to go downtown and watch the parade.

The Hauptstrasse was packed. No vehicles allowed. The streets were lined with people the whole length of Heidelberg's main street.

It was a cold, dark day, but no one noticed. People were dressed in sweaters and heavy coats. All were smiling at winter's sudden demise.

To see over the crowds, some people were standing on storefront window sills. Many second and third-floor windows were open, with people leaning out to see the floats and the marchers.

Many had beer bottles and were drinking. Young ladies were kissing strangers on the street. The essence was to be silly, foolish, and wild. *What a party!* Bob thought.

Some of the marchers wore papier-mâché masks. Incredibly lifelike masks in the form of giant heads, they might have been poking fun at known public figures. Anything goes during Fasching. All could be forgiven.

Floats installed on flatbed trucks went by, and people in colorful costumes waved to the crowds. The front of one of the trucks was decorated to look like the face of a giant character. Another float contained a replica of the old bridge with its two columnar towers. A third float had a huge papier-mâché character facing front on top of the cab and a group of elegantly dressed townspeople riding in the center. A fashionable-looking lady on the truck waved to the crowd while holding a large, half-drunk bottle of beer. A man on the float held a large beer bottle while someone else drank from it. Bob loved the German beer bottles that had a built-in porcelain and rubber stopper connected to the bottle by a metal flange. It was a brilliant way to keep the beer fresh for longer.

Bob, Charlie, and Frank got separated for a while during the parade. They found one another near the university on the Hauptstrasse. Each of them had two beers and was enjoying them during the parade.

"Wow!" Bob said. "These floats are amazing. This is how to enjoy yourself during the winter."

Frank and Charlie agreed.

Charlie, who had still been moping about the loss of Linda, smiled a big smile. "I just met a girl named Gudrun," he said. "She came up to me and kissed me. I liked it, and I think she did too. She gave me her telephone number."

"You dog! Did you talk to her?" Frank asked.

"She is a student at the university."

"Awesome," Bob said. "First time I have seen your old smile back. You better arrange to see her soon."

They hung out there, watching the rest of the parade go by, then headed back to the base together.

In an incredible coincidence, it turned out that February 27 also marked the beginning of the end of the Vietnam War. That evening, Walter Cronkite of CBS News, one of the most respected and trusted journalists in America, reported on his just-finished trip to see the Vietnam situation for himself. He held Americans' trust precisely because he rarely interjected his opinions into the news he reported.

He now expressed his opinion, however, shocking the nation. At the end of his news broadcast, he said, "It seems now more certain than ever that the bloody experience of Vietnam is to end in a stalemate… It is increasingly clear to this reporter that the only rational way out then will be to negotiate, not as victors, but as an honorable people who lived up to their pledge to defend democracy, and did the best they could."

So, on February 27, 1968, Walter Cronkite gave America his permission to end the Vietnam War.

On hearing about Cronkite's broadcast, President Johnson said, "If I've lost Cronkite, I've lost the middle class."

1968 was a presidential election year, and events had finally caught up with Lyndon Johnson. On March 31, 1968, he held a TV news conference and announced two things to the American people. The first was a partial halt to the bombing in North Vietnam. The second was that he would not run for reelection to a second term as president of the United States.

In Heidelberg, Bob's circle of friends breathed a little easier. It seemed that the war in Vietnam was now destined to end.

# Chapter Eight – Berlin and Paris, Spring '68

With April, the weather warmed up and Heidelberg came back to life. Although it rained often, the town became busy again. The tourists began to trickle back and the university area was again filled with young people. Bob and his friends started to feel connected to the town again.

But they had no time to lose either. With just six months left for most of them, they were determined to kick into a higher travel gear, to see and do whatever they could before they had to return to the States.

But just then, back home, politics turned ugly and things started blowing up.

Bob and his friends were shocked to learn that Martin Luther King was assassinated on April 4, 1968, only five years after he gave his famous "I have a dream" speech on the steps of the Lincoln Memorial.

On March 29, King had gone to Memphis, Tennessee, to support the black sanitary public works employees who were on strike. He addressed a rally and gave his "I've been to the mountaintop" speech on April 3.

On April 4, at the Lorraine Motel, he was shot and killed as he stood on the motel's second-floor balcony. Later,

James Earl Ray pled guilty to the murder and was sentenced to 99 years in prison.

In mid-April, Bob made his regular call to Sarah. Things were far from perfect there. Henry and Anna had split up for the moment.

"What caused that?" Bob asked.

"They didn't agree about where to live after marriage. They were also bored with working together at the same computer service company for so many years," Sarah said. "I hope it's just a phase and they get back together soon."

"They'd better. Life is too short for this," Bob said, indulging in a new kind of wisdom he thought he had achieved from his travels in Europe.

Sarah was in good health, as was Yolande and her family, but politics in America were in disarray. Sarah described to Bob what she had been reading. "Anti-war demonstrations are going on everywhere. And violent race riots are happening after Martin Luther King's assassination."

Right after King's assassination, a series of race riots broke out in Washington D.C., along with riots in a total of 110 cities. On April 5, President Johnson called out the National Guard to assist in quelling the riots, but ultimately thirteen people were killed and about 1,000 injured before the riots ended.

President Johnson tried to quell the riots by jawboning on the telephone. He called civil rights leaders, mayors, and governors, to no avail. "I'm not getting through," Johnson told his aides.

In the Bronx, as elsewhere, there was much looting for a couple of weeks right after King's murder.

At the end of the call, Sarah told Bob the neighborhood's silver-lining story. Warner's Fish Market, very popular among the black residents of the neighborhood, was never touched by the looters.

"Wow! How did that happen?" Bob asked.

"Well, many of Warner's regular customers are black," Sarah said. "On April 5, a black woman and her husband came into the store for their weekly fish purchase as usual. Before they left, they gave Warner a large photo of Martin Luther King and asked him to place it in his window. So, this neighborhood black couple, who had taken Warner's advice about which fish to buy for many years, now gave him some advice. 'Put this photo in your store window. It may protect your store from looting, so please do it.' Warner, a smart man, took that advice. When all the looting took place in the neighborhood, his store was never touched."

Meanwhile, in Heidelberg, a trip to Berlin was next on the agenda for Bob, Frank, Arnie, and Charlie. With a buddy stationed there, Frank had taken charge of the Berlin plan.

Frank relayed the intel about Berlin he had heard from his buddy. "There is an overnight train from Frankfurt. Because Berlin is in East Germany, under Russian control, only a military train is allowed to make the trip. All passes, ID cards, and approvals to go to Berlin are inspected at the border by both the U.S. border guards and the East Germans. Zero tolerance for error! And, as East Berlin is also under Russian control, U.S. soldiers have to be in uniform to visit there. No exceptions!"

The four applied for three-day passes and travel permits to East Berlin and began to get their work in order. They would leave in one week, toward the end of April. The trip would be exciting, but they didn't really know what to expect. With their time in Europe quickly coming to an end, they felt this trip to Berlin, in U.S. Army uniform, would somehow be a culmination of their experience in Germany.

The work at the office barreled along as they got ready for the trip. Bob had received several police reports, replies from the families, and army records from the U.S. Army Records Center in St. Louis, Missouri, regarding the Line of Duty investigations. While still unfinished, they were up to date.

A big flap occurred during the week before departure. The four-star general in command of U.S. Army Europe in Heidelberg had his own train with its own train driver. The privilege of office, Bob guessed. Well, because someone had not been paying attention, the train driver's tour of duty in Europe had expired and he'd received orders to report back to the States. Then, all hell broke loose! George Hansen got called into Captain Hall's office.

"George, we could be in for an embarrassment here. We need to fix this now. I want you to drop everything and get this resolved today. The general needs this guy here, period. Now, get out of here and make it happen."

"Yes, sir," George said. "I'll get on it right now."

George skipped lunch that day. He was on the phone for the next eight hours with several offices in Washington D.C. By 10 pm Heidelberg time, the general's train driver had his tour of service in Europe extended for another year.

"Phew!" George exclaimed to Frank and Bob the next day. "This could have been bad. When a four-star is unhappy with you, you don't know where that might lead."

Bob and the others breathed a sigh of relief. The three-day trip to Berlin was still on. Bob also knew that the Seventh Army would go on maneuvers again when he got back. He needed to be in position to help out Sergeant Major Tucker again.

The day before the Berlin trip was easy. All was squared away. Frank, Bob, Arnie, and Charlie went for dinner at the Enlisted Men's club. Fats and His Cats were playing, so it would be a fun night.

Bob got back to his room at about 4:30. He showered, put on some slacks and a sweater, and headed over to the club. The others were already there. They ordered dinner and discussed the trip. They all had cheeseburgers and fries. Now was not the time for diet improvement.

Charlie was in good spirits. He told them how much he was looking forward to the trip.

"So how is it going with your new girlfriend?" Bob asked. Charlie's mood had improved lately. Everyone leaned in to hear the details.

"I have seen her four times already. Her family is from northern Germany, near Rostock, the port on the Baltic. Her father works for the brewery there."

"Wow," Frank said. "Good work. You must like each other to have already seen each other so many times."

"She is a very sweet girl," Charlie said. "She is studying environmental science and learning English too. Her English is already good, which is why we are getting along so well. She would like to go to the U.S. sometime."

"Well done," Arnie said. "Does she know that you are a short-timer with only six months left here in Germany?"

"Not yet. I'll have to tell her when we return from Berlin. I don't want to mislead her."

"Think of it as a test," Arnie said. "If she really likes you, it won't matter. Besides, honesty is the best policy in these matters."

"Well, I am all for her," Bob said. "After your nightmare with Linda and the diamond, anyone who can get you smiling again gets my vote."

By then, the club was crowded. Fats and His Cats had begun the first set, and the club was vibrating with energy. The fat man looked awesome in his red dinner jacket. His goatee glistened as he played the electric guitar.

The band played some new songs that were just hitting their highs on the pop charts, including "Lady Madonna" by the Beatles and "The Mighty Quinn" by Manfred Mann. Then the best dancing song of the night, "Cry Like a Baby" by the Box Tops. Their "The Letter" had been a sensation the previous year. The four discussed the next day's departure plans, then headed back to the barracks and turned in for the night.

**Berlin**

The last day at the office was uneventful. All packed and ready to go, the four friends kept a very low profile and left work promptly at 4 pm. Back at the barracks, they showered and changed into their dress uniforms for the trip on the "duty train."

Rich, who wasn't coming along, dropped them at the train station. "Be careful guys," he said. "Who knows what's up in the East? And I won't be around to rescue you."

They laughed and said their goodbyes.

With their reservations for the overnight military train from Frankfurt in hand, they hopped on the train for the one-hour trip to Frankfurt. There, they would catch the 9 pm overnight "Berlin Express."

They arrived in Frankfurt at about 8 pm, a full hour early. The ever-prepared Bob insisted on being early. There would be no missing this train. No messing around! The others had rolled their eyes when Bob insisted, but all gave in.

The Berlin Express was on time. They climbed into one of the cabins that held four passengers and settled in. The train left precisely at 9 pm.

The Berlin Express started running in 1945, just after the war, to provide a route between West and East. The military crew consisted of a train commander, a non-commissioned officer conductor, several military policemen, and a radio operator.

The MPs protected the passengers and enforced regulations governing the behavior of U.S. travelers. Zero tolerance for incidents! While the train was in the Soviet Occupation Zone, no passengers could get off the train or speak to the Russian or East German guards. The only exception was the senior MP who processed the paperwork.

After entering East Germany, the train stopped for inspection. An East German engine was hooked up for the rest of the trip to Berlin.

In the sleeping cabins, Frank, Arnie, Charlie, and Bob got ready to turn in for the night. They ate their snacks, washed up, and got into the cot-like beds. Nothing to see, and a big day ahead!

The train chugged its way through the night. There were no stops during the 110 miles to West Berlin. An occasional train whistle broke the silence, but it was very quiet otherwise.

In the morning, they got ready and left the train. The U.S. military police triple-checked their papers and released them into West Berlin. This was their only trip where every detail of their three-day passes and other documents was carefully checked.

They were not ready for the explosion of modern life they saw.

After leaving the train station, they took two cheap rooms at a hotel nearby, stowed their gear, and started walking. The routine had become a well-used strategy for the first day in a new town.

They hopped on a bus to the Brandenburg Gate, which was located in the Soviet Sector. Staying on the western side, they could see it a short distance across the border.

One of the most widely known German monuments, the Brandenburg Gate was completed in 1791. It consists of twelve Doric columns, six per side, forming five passageways through. At the top of the gate is Quadriga, a sculpture of a chariot drawn by four horses, driven by Victoria, the Roman goddess of victory.

There wasn't a soul near the gate except for one East German soldier on an elevated guardhouse facing the West. An East German flag flew on the top, near the Quadriga.

"What an awesome sight. You can just imagine the conquering armies that might have marched under it," Frank remarked.

The others smiled and took pictures.

From there, they walked over to the Tiergarten to see the Berlin Victory Column, another of Berlin's most visited sites.

Unveiled in 1873, the 220-foot tall column, including the sculpture of Victoria, is built on a base of red granite. At the top, the bronze sculpture of Victoria, the Roman goddess of war, is 27 feet high and weighs 35 tons. They all took more pictures. Frank took Bob's picture in front of the Victory Column. Bob's green quilted ski jacket now had a full, chest-high row of patches displaying the various places he had visited. From there, they walked over to Kurfurstendamm, the main shopping and commercial street.

They were amazed. It was alive with traffic, and hustle and bustle. HONK! HONK! A cacophony of taxi horns sounded. It was as if the impatient Mercedes taxi cabs were demanding others move aside to allow them through faster. Ku'damm, as it was known, was a broad street with low slung modern office buildings and department stores on either side. Big signs proclaimed the businesses within, notably AEG, which became the German version of General Electric and later incorporated into Daimler Benz, and Madame department store.

Double-decker buses moved along and stopped to drop off and pick up passengers. Modern metallic street lights rose up from the sidewalks and curved over the traffic lane to illuminate the streets at night.

Walking in the direction of the Kaiser Wilhelm Memorial Church, they passed a gleaming glass office tower with a huge Mercedes-Benz logo on the roof. Well-dressed people were on the street, walking to work or to breakfast at a café. The sights and sounds were mesmerizing.

They continued walking along the main street of the gleaming metropolis. The ruins of the Kaiser Wilhelm Memorial Church stood, broken but tall, on the Ku'damm as if to say "It's good to live in the present, but let's not forget the past."

On a side street, they stopped for lunch. The street was wide, and the café had the look and atmosphere of a beer garden, with plenty of outdoor tables. An outer black iron fence closed the garden off from the street. The tables were close together. The waitress came over and took their beer order. All the beer was on tap. Bob chose a Lowenbrau. The others ordered Hofbräu. By the time they were on their second beer, the food arrived. Huge portions of chicken and veal sandwiches and salads.

They were in no rush. The sky was bright blue and there were only a few small white clouds. Passers-by were walking right past the fence enclosing their table. The four of them were feeding off the energy of the noise on the street, the passers-by, and the many conversations going on in the beer garden itself.

"Guys, we have done so much already, and it's still morning. What's next?" Bob asked.

"Well, more sightseeing, a nice dinner, and a bar at night will do it for me," said Frank.

"Amen," said Arnie and Charlie.

Charlie smiled. "This is great. This town looks alive with fun."

Frank remembered something. "I just remembered that my friend told me to be sure not to miss the Russian War Memorial. It's right back at the Tiergarten, not far from the Victory Column. Let's go back there after lunch."

Seeing that Charlie was happy in his new relationship with Gudrun, Arnie decided to press for more details about his breakup with Linda.

"Hey, Charlie," he said. "We never did hear the full story of your breakup with Linda. What really happened?"

"Well, I was in no mood to talk back then," Charlie said. "But I got blindsided and got hurt. I don't want to experience that again anytime soon."

"So, what happened?" Bob piled in.

"Well, two things happened. First, she had been seeing someone for several months before I got back there. He's a banker and earns a lot of money. Money was never my biggest motivation, and that's why I was surprised. 'Love is OK,' Linda said. 'But Charlie, how will you take care of me?' She was frightened by the thought of living a less affluent lifestyle than her parents provided. She needs to be taken care of, and she didn't believe I could do that. So that was the big surprise for me: money is so important. Not for itself, but to pay for things that the love of your life can't do without. I know it's easy to say 'well, she wasn't right for you.' But when you are in love, it hurts just the same. When I get back to Boston, you can bet I'll be starting a career that is high paying."

"Sorry," Arnie said. "I feel your pain, my brother. Thanks for sharing that. I feel like I really learned something about you just now."

"And what about the ring," Frank asked. "Why didn't she return it?"

"I still don't know," Charlie said. "But she just gave it to my mom. So it will be there when I get back. I'll sell it and use the money to finance my new high-paying career."

"Well, thanks for confiding in us. It means a lot. But I guess you have to say that it's better to learn all that now rather than ten years down the line when you have two kids, a house, and a mortgage," Frank said.

"Amen, brother," Bob said, and they toasted to that!

After the sandwiches and beer were finished, they paid the check and strolled back to the Tiergarten to see the Russian War Memorial.

This huge, imposing monument is a memorial to the Russian troops lost during WWII. In the Battle of Berlin in April and May 1945 alone, 80,000 Soviet troops were killed. Constructed with the stones from the destroyed Reich Chancellery, it has a curved concrete form, topped by a large statue of a Soviet soldier. It is set in landscaped gardens that are adorned with several pieces of military hardware. They walked around the monument, took more photographs, and called it a day.

Back at the hotel, they relaxed before dinner. They all thanked Frank for making the trip happen. Frank gave most of the credit to his army buddy who had provided all the intel.

"We go through Checkpoint Charlie tomorrow, but it has to be in uniform," Frank reminded them. "My friend also told me we have to go to the Blue Lion club one night. It is the hottest club in town and doesn't open until 11 pm."

"Let's do that tonight," Arnie said. They all agreed and nodded approvingly.

While Bob, Frank, Charlie, and Arnie were enjoying Berlin, the social upheaval of the late 1960s was going on around them, in Germany, as well as in other parts of the world.

In the weeks before they arrived in Berlin, Rudi Dutschke, a political activist in the German student movement, was shot right near his home at 140 Kurfurstendamm. It was an assassination attempt.

Later in April and May in West Germany, there were mass student protests that became known as the 1968 Movement. The students later came to be known as "the 68ers" or "the 1968 generation."

Students around the world had become disillusioned with their governments. In West Germany, they opposed some government politicians being too closely aligned with Germany's Nazi past and they protested the United States' war in Vietnam. They were opposed to the consumer culture, wanted liberation for third-world countries, and some also embraced communal living and sexual liberation.

In the U.S., young people were experimenting with LSD. Rock bands such as the Grateful Dead, Jefferson Airplane, and even the Beatles had tried it. In the mid-1960s, a new music genre called acid rock got underway. This music was characterized by heavy, distorted guitar riffs and drug-referencing lyrics.

In December 1966, Buffalo Springfield released a song called "For What It's Worth (Stop, Hey What's That Sound)." The song was actually a reaction to strict curfews enacted on Sunset Strip in Hollywood, California. Local residents and businesses objected to the late-night noise and traffic congestion and lobbied the local authorities to establish a curfew. On November 12, as many as 1,000 young people, including some celebrities, gathered to protest the curfew enforcement. Trouble broke out and continued through November and December, forcing some clubs to shut down.

"Stop, Hey What's That Sound" became one of the most important anti-war songs of the generation. It became a powerful shorthand symbol for the volatile atmosphere of the 1960s counterculture and protest movement.

Back in West Berlin, the foursome put on their best casual slacks and shirts. They went to dinner at an inexpensive German restaurant near the hotel. Dinner was uneventful.

After dinner, they stopped for coffee at a local café to kill some time. Then they took a taxi cab to the Blue Lion club. After waiting in line for an hour, they got in and were seated at a table in the back. The room was packed, with hardly any room between tables to squeeze through. The bandstand was a semi-circle facing the tables, and the bar was on the other side, closer to the front door. When people moved between the tables, you almost had to help them get through. The show was starting, and the dance floor was getting crowded. It was a combination of new age and dance music, and the young crowd loved it.

The guys ordered a bottle of wine and sat back to enjoy the show. It was hard to talk because the noise was so loud. On the way to the men's room, Bob ran his fingers over the fabric covering the room's walls. The rich texture lent a sense of elegance to the room. Very different from the bare-bones interior of the Enlisted Men's club in Heidelberg.

They quickly noticed the most unusual feature of the Blue Lion. Each table had a telephone. A laminated binder on the tabletop had a map of the room with the telephone extension of every table. Holy cow! You could call any table in the room. None of them had ever seen anything like that before. Not even Frank, who had hung out in Los Angeles. Wow!

Of course, none of them spoke German, so the telephone was of little use. Still, the telephones, along with the opulent ambiance, set the club apart. In the years since, Bob has never again seen telephones in a club.

After the first set, the band took a break, but the din continued. When the band returned, Frank ordered another bottle of wine, and they enjoyed the rest of the show. They left just before the end of the show at around 3 am. A taxi took them back to the hotel. They needed to get some rest. That day, they were going to East Berlin.

**Checkpoint Charlie**

Checkpoint Charlie was on Friedrichstrasse. It was the only way that U.S. soldiers could visit East Berlin. Soldiers had to be in uniform and with papers strictly in order for both the U.S. and East German checkpoints.

In uniform, the guys took a taxi over to the checkpoint. The sight was sobering. Suddenly, they were even prouder than usual to be in the uniform of the United States of America.

All along the East-West perimeter, there were two-meter high wire fences with concrete block guardhouses every so often. About three meters in front of the fence, stretching for miles, two rows of anchored hedgehogs (a group of three interlocked metallic girders) were installed to prevent vehicles from passing.

Checkpoint Charlie itself was nondescript. Friedrichstrasse was a wide street. From the allied side, you could see some buildings in East Berlin. At the center of the street was a small portable shed, only seven feet high, with windows all around. There was a U.S. flag flying on a flagpole in front. The U.S. Army had deliberately not erected any permanent structure there to highlight that they considered it a temporary situation. They never considered the inner Berlin boundary an international border.

The name Checkpoint Charlie stemmed from the NATO phonetic alphabet. It was the third checkpoint named, and thus called Charlie. Nothing more complicated than that.

They walked up to a window. Inside were U.S. Army military police.

The MPs carefully checked their paperwork and let them through. A little further down the street, the East Germans did the same, and the four soldiers passed into East Berlin along Friedrichstrasse. They had agreed: no funny business, no detours, and a unanimous vote to do anything out of the ordinary. No messing around!

As they walked along the main street, they were hit with the sheer desolation they saw everywhere. West Berlin had returned to prosperity, with modern gleaming office towers, department stores filled with merchandise, and cars of every make and model cruising the avenues. A few streets away, here in East Berlin, it was the opposite. The bombs of WWII could have been dropped here the previous week. Many buildings were still half-destroyed and there were few people on the street and very few, old-fashioned-looking automobiles. Compared to the hustle and bustle of the West Berlin streets, the silence here was deafening.

The solemnity of it was almost paralyzing. The contrast between East and West was staggering. Continuing down the main avenue, they turned onto another wide street. On the opposite side, there was a large department store. The façade was crumbling. A line of people, dressed for the colder weather, was waiting to get into the store. The store windows had little on display.

The austere faces of those in line added a somber note to the walk. Not a smile among the twenty or thirty of them. And not much chatter going on. All deadly serious.

A few blocks over to the west, it was just the opposite. All was possible there, where smiling faces and chatter proclaimed good times and abundance.

It was a sobering experience for Bob, Frank, Arnie, and Charlie. They exchanged looks but did not speak. After walking a few more blocks, always on a wide street, they turned around and retraced their steps to Checkpoint Charlie. They felt a sense of unease and danger here in the East.

Crossing back to the West was no different. Their papers were again carefully checked, especially in the East, where the military police were watchful to prevent East Berliners from defecting. After crossing, they all breathed a sigh of relief, as if they had just "escaped" from East Germany. Of course, escape to the West was far easier for them, in U.S. Army uniforms.

Back in West Berlin, Bob said, "Damn! That's why we are here, isn't it?" The others nodded but did not speak.

They took a taxi back to the hotel. Back in their civvies (civilian clothes), they went to dinner near the hotel. Later, they went back to the hotel and turned in early. Early the next morning, they boarded the train, in their dress uniforms, for the long trip back to Heidelberg. The border security checks were the same as before but in reverse.

Back in Heidelberg, they discussed the trip over dinner at the Enlisted Men's club. Rich was there with a couple of the other guys who had not gone. They were eager to hear the details of the trip.

"Frank, we owe you for that one," Bob said. "You got some great information from your buddy. The trip went smoothly from start to finish."

"The Brandenburg Gate and the other monuments were nice, but the main thing we learned was about the military standoff between East and West at Checkpoint Charlie and East Berlin," Arnie added. "It was awesome. I have never seen people as downcast as those East Berliners."

"Me neither," Charlie agreed. "It was seriously bad. I didn't feel very safe in East Berlin. They want you in uniform when you go there, and now I know why. When we passed through the East German checkpoint on the way back, I was very glad to be in uniform."

"I was glad we got to go to the Blue Lion club. It was special. It reminded me of some of the clubs in Los Angeles," Frank said.

"So what was the Blue Lion like?" Rich asked.

"It was very upscale," Frank said. "The crowd was young but well dressed, and the music was great. Did we tell you about the telephones? Every table had a telephone.

You could call any table in the place. If only we knew some German, we would have met some girls for sure."

"Well done, Frank. I see I made a mistake in not going along. We are all short-timers now, but maybe I can go there in the summer," Rich said. "But I have arranged to go to London to visit my grandparents in June. I'll fly for free on a cargo plane, courtesy of the U.S. Air Force, from Frankfurt to London."

"Wow!" Frank said. "Impressive!"

Dinner was finished, and the band was ending their first set. It was mainly rock and roll and dance music. The bikini-clad go-go dancers accompanying the band were dancing on the area of the bandstand that jutted out toward the audience.

Charlie looked at them and smiled. "Now that we're back, we can resume our good life in Heidelberg. Maybe we'll meet some girls here tonight."

The others laughed, knowing that could never happen in the Enlisted Men's club. They had tried and failed countless times already. Finally, after all the Berlin stories were told and the last drinks were finished, they left the club and turned in for the night.

Back from Berlin, the four men were grateful to be Americans, and especially to be part of the U.S. Army. They had felt a sense of danger and unease in East Berlin. They suddenly knew at an emotional level why the Seventh Army tanks were there in Germany, and why they staged maneuvers several times a year. They were the bulwark of the West.

**Paris Revisited**

Keenly feeling their short-timer status (set to return to the States in a short five months), they all wanted to keep up the pace of travel, but Frank and Charlie had other plans for May, and Rich was heading for London. So only Bob and Arnie headed back to Paris at the beginning of May.

Bob and Arnie got more than they bargained for. The travel went smoothly. The three-day passes and the overnight train to Paris were so familiar now that they thought nothing of it. But on their first day in Paris, they sensed a different vibe than before. They enjoyed the cafés, speaking the French language, and the beautiful sights. They even went to the Louvre to see the Mona Lisa. But things felt different in Paris.

They walked past massive student demonstrations. Students were protesting against capitalism, consumerism, the American war in Vietnam, and the government institutions that were totally out of touch with the students and the French workers. Heavy repression of the protests by the police led to large-scale sympathy strikes by trade unions that eventually involved more than eleven million French workers.

Although Bob and Charlie did not see any violence early in May, violent protests erupted later that month, in the Latin Quarter, right where they were staying. On Friday,

May 10, a huge crowd congregated on the Rive Gauche. Confrontations with the police lasted into the next morning, and there were hundreds of arrests and injuries. A million people marched in Paris that day.

By the end of May, it was out of control.

On May 30, President de Gaulle dissolved the National Assembly and called for a new election on June 23, ordering workers back to work at the same time. From that time, the revolutionary movement started to fade. New elections were held in June, resulting in a sweeping victory for the Gaullists.

Bob and Arnie saw some sights and enjoyed their days in Paris. On their last day, they visited the Eiffel Tower. It was a beautiful sunny day, not a cloud in the sky. They walked around the tower and took photos of each other. As they left, an American tourist asked if they had seen the Statue of Liberty.

"What?" Bob said. "That's in New York."

"Sure, it is," the tourist said. "But there is also a smaller one here in Paris a few miles down the Seine, that way." He pointed south. "The French have kept a replica here to remind everyone of the statue and its meaning."

"Wow! We have got to go see that. Thanks," Bob said.

"Enjoy your day."

"Arnie, let's go find it."

They walked along the Seine for a mile or two until the statue came into view. Located in the middle of the river, it was placed on a small island called the Isle des Cygnes. Bob and Arnie got closer and finally were able to take one of the best photos of the trip: The Statue of Liberty with the Eiffel Tower in the background.

"Hey Arnie, take a picture of me in front of both of them."

Arnie took the shot, then Bob took one of Arnie using Arnie's camera. Bob treasured that photo as one of the best they had taken.

Later that evening, Bob realized the inescapable fact that although he had grown up within a few miles of the large Statue of Liberty in New York, he had not once visited it. After seeing East Berlin, he now realized the New York statue's importance and vowed to visit it as soon as he returned home.

The next day, they boarded the train and returned to Heidelberg.

After seeing the Paris student demonstrations, they wondered what the heck was happening in the world. They had mixed feelings about the things they had seen. Part of them felt connected to the whole student movement, protesting how out of touch with the youth generation the world's governments were. But, at the same time, having seen the sad faces in East Berlin and the Statue of Liberty side by side with the Eiffel Tower in Paris, they were proud to be Americans and proud to be serving their country in the U.S. Army.

Back at Campbell Barracks, they were grateful that Heidelberg was a calm port in the revolutionary storm. They hoped they could make the most of their last few months there before returning home.

# Chapter Nine – Return

June arrived along with the Seventh Army tank maneuvers, two weeks of joint exercises to showcase the abilities of the U.S. Army Tank Corps. The "Bulwark of the West" put itself on display several times a year so the Russians would know not to mess around.

Bob got a call from Sergeant Major Tucker at the beginning of June. Despite being expected, the call still came as a surprise. In three days, he would temporarily be reassigned to the Seventh Army to help set up the headquarters for the maneuvers.

Same as before, only in a different location. Keep 'em guessing, right?

He met Tucker to get his assignment.

"Bob, this time we're going to Grafenwoehr," Tucker said. "We'll use the U.S. Army barracks there. The setup will be the same as before. I want you to set up the command post and HQ, and report back to me. I'll come out after two days and test it all out. The exercises will start the following day."

"I see," Bob said with a nod.

"We have to get this right. This will be an extensive series of exercises. The tank platoons will demonstrate the ability to maneuver, shoot effectively, and maintain secure communications. Don't fail me, Bob," Tucker said. "I need this to go off without a hitch. There have been some concerns about Russian troop movements recently, and our four-star in Heidelberg will be watching these exercises closely. The Department of the Army will be watching too."

"You can count on me, Sergeant Major."

"Czechoslovakia is only two hours from Grafenwoehr, and there may be trouble brewing there," Tucker continued. "After Dubcek's rise to power in January, he has been instituting democratic reforms. The Russians have warned him about going too far. Our high command is very concerned about Russian troop and tank movements in the area. That's why these exercises will be observed even more closely than usual."

Temporary reassignment approved, Bob picked up his army Jeep and driver and left Heidelberg three days later.

He arrived at Grafenwoehr four hours later and set up his bunk in the U.S. Army barracks there. His roommate was Sergeant Smith, with whom he had worked the last time. This time, the headquarters would be right on the army base, in a small administration building that was used intermittently as classroom space.

Bob and Sergeant Smith spent two days setting up everything like the last time. At the U.S. Army base at

Grafenwoehr, the communications were solid and reliable and everything was easier. It all went right on the first try.

At the end of the second day, Bob informed Sergeant Major Tucker that everything was set up and the command-control room, security measures, and all the communications were solid and functioning. Still, Tucker asked Bob to remain one more day to be on hand when he tested it all. Bob understood. He would have done the same thing.

Tucker arrived the next day and spent two hours reviewing and testing everything in the headquarters. Finally, he gave Bob a wide smile and thumbs up. Tucker was someone you did not want to disappoint, and Bob never did.

Bob got a ride back to Heidelberg and resumed his normal life. The office, the bowling alleys, the Enlisted Men's club, and downtown Heidelberg. It was all swell!

The pea-green Beetle, long repaired, was now back in use. The local Schwimmbad had opened in May. Starting the first weekend in June, Bob and his buddies drove the Beetle there every weekend. It was crowded but fun.

Arnie and Charlie were good swimmers, and Charlie could dive off the platform. He'd learned to dive growing up in Boston. Bob just swam. He found a lane and did laps. He enjoyed the exercise. It reminded him of swimming at Orchard Beach in the Bronx. There, he would go slightly offshore and swim parallel to the shoreline for a long time, to cool off as much as for the exercise.

One day, Bob, Charlie, and Arnie left the Schwimmbad at around 5 pm. They piled into the Beetle and headed to the Inn at Neckargemünd for dinner. They were planning to meet Frank there.

They got a table in a corner and ordered the Porterhouse steak, the house specialty. The steak was always large enough for two, and it never disappointed. Over beers, they discussed the few months they had left.

Frank had just spoken with his uncle, the largest Chevrolet Oldsmobile dealer in Los Angeles. He was all pumped up about returning to Los Angeles and making it big. Arnie was starting to look forward to heading to Jacksonville, Florida. His plan to go into insurance underwriting was still in play. He had been reading some books on insurance and was excited.

Bob lifted a glass to toast. "This is sweet and sad at the same time. It sort of marks the end of an era of great friendships and great experiences."

Frank and the others lifted their glasses and drank the toast.

"Maybe it doesn't need to end here. Why don't we have a reunion next year to celebrate all our accomplishments in this coming year?" Charlie said.

"Hear, hear," everyone called. They drank another toast.

Bob had more mixed feelings than the others about the ending of this great era. He was concerned because he knew he had no plan and no helpful contacts back home to get him started. He knew two things so far: he had no plan and he seriously needed one.

But, at the same time, he felt the most hopeful he had ever been. He knew that he had been transformed over the past two years. He was more worldly, more confident, and his life was now filled with experiences that he couldn't have dreamed of while walking the streets of the Bronx two years before. He knew for sure that although he had no plan now, he would be unstoppable the moment he got one.

Five days into the Seventh Army's two-week exercise, Bob got an urgent call from Sergeant Major Tucker.

"Bob, there is a problem with the exercises. I need you to get out there and fix it."

"What do you want me to do, Sergeant Major?" Bob asked.

"This is a one-day task, and it has to happen tomorrow. I have already cleared it with Captain Hall. Just come on over and let's discuss it. I don't want to talk about it on the phone."

"Sure," Bob said. "I'm on my way. See you in ten minutes."

Ten minutes later, Tucker explained the situation. "First of all, this is a confidential matter. Even Captain Hall does not know the details. You can't ever talk about it."

"No problem," Bob said.

"Sometimes, on these exercises, there are some folks who are not really on the roster but who are asked to pitch in in various ways to make the exercises run smoother. Now, it turns out there are some extra folks at the exercises right now, helping out. It's like having twelve men on the field in the NFL. Bob, something has come up and we need to get over there and get them out of there by tomorrow morning, without fail. We have got to make sure that the penalty flag doesn't get dropped on them. These guys are the defense of the West. You don't want to mess with them. They are heroes, for heaven's sake."

"I see," Bob said.

"I need you to drive out there tomorrow morning and extract these six guys. Jeep and driver will be waiting for you at the motor pool at 3 am along with a light truck. You need to arrive at Grafenwoehr by 8 am, no later. The commander on the ground is expecting you. You will scoop up the six civilians and head back here pronto. Any questions?"

"No. I've got it. But who are these guys? Why are they there in the first place?"

"Look," Tucker said. "Bob, you have been doing a great job for me since you've been here. I know you are a short-timer with only about three months left here. Sometimes it's better not to know something. This is such a time. You only know you've been asked to bring them here. Let's keep it that way."

"Of course, Sergeant Major. I see," said Bob. "I'll be at the motor pool at 3 am."

And with that, Bob turned and left.

Bob did not go out with his buddies that night. He just relaxed on his bunk after dinner and went to sleep early. Using an alarm clock was totally foreign to Bob. But that night was different. He borrowed one from Arnie and set it for 2 am.

"What do you need this for? This is not the Bob I know," Arnie said.

Bob smiled. "You're right Arnie, But it's different tonight. I have to hook up with the Seventh Army early tomorrow morning. I can't afford to be late."

"OK. Good luck," Arnie said. He handed Bob the alarm clock and headed out to the Enlisted Men's club.

Bob lay on his bunk and thought about his remaining time there. He wondered how it would all work out. He knew somehow that all would go smoothly on this end. He was more concerned about what would happen when he got back home to the Bronx.

He needed a plan but had none. He owed money to Aunt Yolande and had promised to pay it back quickly. Could he convince her to let the loan ride so he could quickly get his new life moving? He racked his brain for how to prepare for his homecoming. Who could he contact to get a start in business? Were any of his old friends still around? Had they progressed in life while he was away? Would they give him a helping hand up or drag him down? He couldn't think of anyone who could help him.

*You will have to start from ground zero and have only yourself to rely on,* he thought. *That will be the hard part. But look at what you've done in the past two years. You can do anything now.*

He fell asleep in an optimistic frame of mind. At least he now knew what questions needed answering.

BBBBring! BBBBring! BBBBring! The alarm clock went off precisely at 2 am. Bob quickly turned over and pushed down the button so no one else would awaken. He had shaved before going to bed, so he was ahead of the game. He threw on his military fatigues.

His shirt arm patch was an eagle with a yellow stripe under it, showing he was a specialist with a rank of E5. It was the fifth NCO rank from the bottom, equivalent to the rank of sergeant. That was normally the highest rank a two-year term of service would allow.

Bob arrived at the motor pool at precisely 3 am. The truck and Jeep were waiting as promised. He hopped into the Jeep and said, "Let's go." The driver punched down on the gas, and the Jeep screeched forward. The truck started up slowly but followed along.

"What is this all about?" the Jeep driver asked. "Must be important to be on the road at 3 am."

Bob immediately realized the wisdom of Sergeant Major Tucker. "I don't know any more than you. We are just picking up six people and bringing them back to Heidelberg," he said with a smile.

The trip on the highway was uneventful, and there was little conversation. Although there was no speed limit, their orders were to stay below 65 mph. No accidents. Not this morning, not ever!

They swung into the barracks at Grafenwoehr at around 7:30 am and headed directly for the Seventh Army's temporary headquarters. The command post was already bustling with activity. Bob checked in with the exercise commander, a full bird colonel, who took him to the conference room where the six civilians were waiting.

They were dressed in civilian clothes and had their bags packed. Good to go! The commander introduced Bob to the civilians and told them they were under Bob's authority and on their way to Heidelberg.

"Sir, thank you for your help," Bob said, saluting. The full bird colonel saluted back.

Bob turned to the civilians. "All right, gentlemen, let's go. We should be back in Heidelberg in about four hours."

Following Bob out of the barracks, they hopped into the waiting truck. Bob jumped back into the Jeep and spoke to the driver. "Let's hit it. To Heidelberg. Remember, still under 65 mph, please. No slip-ups."

The trip back was also uneventful. The Jeep driver again asked Bob what it was all about, but Bob just repeated what he'd said before. "You know as much as I do. We are just taking these guys to Heidelberg."

At around 1 pm, the mini convoy arrived back at Campbell Barracks. They stopped in front of the motor pool. Bob got out and escorted the six civilians to a conference room in the motor pool building and asked them to wait there, then went over to Sergeant Major Tucker's office. Tucker put the phone down and looked at Bob expectantly without saying a word.

"Mission accomplished, Sergeant Major," Bob said. "The six civilians are in the motor pool conference room awaiting further instructions."

Sergeant Major Tucker's face broke out into a wide toothy grin, showing his immaculate white teeth. "Great job, Bob. You have done the Seventh Army a service today." He paused, then asked, "Did it go smoothly? Any hitches?"

"No," Bob said. "All went like clockwork. The Jeep driver was curious about what was going on. But I truthfully told him I did not know."

Tucker smiled, got up, came around his desk, and shook Bob's hand. To Bob, it was the equivalent of getting a medal.

"Thanks again. You are off duty now. You can go back to your regular job."

Bob went back to the office in high spirits.

**July**

At the beginning of July, Bob, Arnie, and Frank were called into Captain Hall's office.

"I want to tell you that we have several new recruits who may be your replacements," Hall said. "They are at the Frankfurt reassignment station now, and they have been initially qualified. They have college degrees and high aptitude scores on the U.S. Army test battery, just like yourselves. So, this is your last chance to remain here. If you enlist for three more years, I'll arrange for you to remain here, along with a promotion. What do you say?"

Although Hall had spoken with a straight face, he started smiling when Bob and the others began to laugh. They had never shared a joke like that with Captain Hall before. Captain Hall broke out in a wide grin.

"Speaking for myself," Bob said, "I have been happy working here. Not only have I met great people but I have also been able to serve in the U.S. Army. But that said, I can't wait to get back home and start my life."

Arnie and Frank chimed in and told Hall about how far advanced their plans were: Frank with the auto dealership and Arnie with the insurance business in Jacksonville.

Captain Hall was gracious. He complimented them on their work there and gave them his best wishes for success. "So here is the number of the reassignment station in Frankfurt. Call Sergeant Ames there. He has done the preliminary vetting of the six potential new team members. Now that you three have less than sixty days to go until your departure, we can take three of them to replace you."

"Thank you, sir," they all said and left the office.

They called Sergeant Ames. Frank and Arnie were senior, so they each took three names and interviewed them on the phone. Bob went back to work.

They selected three, and the recruits arrived at Heidelberg one week later. They were given rooms in the same barracks and spare desks in the office. Suddenly Bob's replacement was there! That made things definite! The prospect of going home had become real. Several more recruits arrived over the next few weeks. There were less than sixty days to train them.

Bob's replacement was Ralph. He was from New York City and had just graduated from NYU. He had been drafted, had no love for the war, and no love for the army, but he was happy to do his service in Heidelberg. So were the others. However, a conflict erupted over the next month as Ralph found fault with the system and the way things were done. Finally, after a couple of weeks, Bob had had enough of him. Bob took him aside and said, "You know, Ralph, there is no law that says you have to work here. You seem to find fault with everything we do here. I suggest you either get over it or go see Captain Hall. You could tell him this group is not to your liking. I'm sure he would help you find another assignment pronto. Otherwise, just get over it. If you do, I promise you will enjoy living here in Heidelberg."

Ralph seemed to back off after that talk. It was as if he hadn't previously considered that his assignment could be in a far worse place. Over the next few weeks, Ralph slowly began to see the advantages for him in remaining. He stopped complaining. He had a degree in economics from NYU and was smart. He picked up the work easily. After about five weeks, Ralph had mastered it all and Bob could relax.

They might have gotten closer, but Ralph could not get past the chip on his shoulder from being involuntarily called into the army. However, Bob was happy that he was smart and fully capable of doing the job. By August, Bob was able to spend a little less time on actual work and more time just advising Ralph.

The other guys had the same experience. Their replacements were all smart and capable, so they, too, could focus more time on their return home. There were personal possessions to ship home, sell, or give away. There were arrangements to be made with relatives or friends back home who could help them hit the ground running when they arrived. There were travel arrangements. The standard way back home was a commercial airline flight from Frankfurt to JFK International Airport. From there, on to Fort Dix, New Jersey. At Fort Dix, you would be released from the army. For Bob, it would then be a bus ride into Manhattan and a train to the Bronx. For the others, it was a further flight to Jacksonville, Los Angeles, or Chicago.

They were determined to enjoy their last days in the Enlisted Men's club, downtown Heidelberg, and the local restaurants and jazz clubs. They all agreed how lucky they were to be leaving in September, at the end of the wonderful weather, and at the height of Heidelberg's busy season.

Toward the end of July, Jack and Becky Custis decided to host another house party. They were leaving in September, so this would be the final house party for the "old guard," most of whom would also leave in September.

On Saturday, after Jeep maintenance, Bob and Charlie drove downtown. They parked and walked along the Hauptstrasse. It was packed with tourists. They walked to the old bridge and back, had sandwiches and a beer in an outdoor café, and headed back. Life was good!

They arrived at Jack and Becky's at around 6 pm. Bob brought a bottle of Johnnie Walker Black, as was his custom. Charlie brought two six-packs of German beer. They knew this might be the last get-together for them.

"This could be our last party," Bob said. "You know, Charlie suggested maybe we should have a reunion next year. We would need someone to host it, of course."

"You don't mean us," Sam replied. "I'm going to have my work cut out for me. I'll be back at the auto plant. It's great money but hard work."

"Well, I'll be taking it easy I suppose," Cindy broke in. "I could do most of the work. Come on, Sam, we should host it."

She gave him a look that was sweet and dangerous all at once. Sam was a stubborn guy, but this time he gave in right away.

Cheers broke out and a toast was made. "To the reunion in Chicago next year. Hurrah!"

Frank recounted the trip to Berlin for those who hadn't heard it.

"Don't forget the telephones at the Blue Lion," Bob said.

"Checkpoint Charlie too," Charlie added.

They listened to some great music on the stereo that would be shipped back to Richmond the following week.

That was how it worked as the time got shorter. You wanted to use something one more time and then ship it home or sell it.

Becky loved to dance and had just bought some new singles at the record store on the Hauptstrasse that week. "Lady Madonna" by the Beatles had come out recently. They played that and then "Mony Mony" by Tommy James and the Shondells, followed by the best dance song of the summer, "Jumpin' Jack Flash" by the Rolling Stones.

"Why are you still buying music?" Frank asked Becky. "Aren't you two leaving in September?"

"Sure," Becky said. "But we don't have flight reservations yet. Probably in a week or two. So we'll ship back the stereo equipment and most of our clothing next week. There is plenty of time."

Rich told them about visiting his grandparents in England in June. The flight on the U.S.A.F. cargo plane had been uncomfortable but free. He had taken a bus into London and then another one to Maidstone, just southeast of London. He'd stayed with his grandparents for four days and driven all over the beautiful countryside there.

"I didn't know my great grandfather was in the British Army in World War I," he said.

Charlie seemed really happy. They asked him about Gudrun. Charlie said they were still together. He had even visited her parents in Rostock the previous week.

"They are nice people," Charlie said. "Her father is a beer brewer at the Rostock brewery. We drank some really good beer together, and they seemed to like me."

Arnie flashed Charlie a look. "Well, that sounds serious. What are you thinking?"

"Well, I have to go home in mid-September. She knows that and is OK with it. I have to get started working. She will come over to visit in six months when she graduates."

"Wow! Are you sure about this?" Bob asked.

"Well, nothing is certain," Charlie said. "I found that out with Linda. But things are good between us. We both want it to last, and I have to give it a chance."

"It sounds great," Arnie said. "A toast to Charlie and Gudrun. May they be together forever."

They all drank.

"Bob, what are your plans?" Sam asked.

"I can't wait to get started. I want to move into Manhattan, get a job and a car. With my degree in economics, I'll look for a job on Wall Street. It will be tough at first, I know, because I don't have any contacts. But I will make it. There are no other options."

That evening, the food, drink, and music went on for a long time. When they had run their course, the friends slept in whichever room they were in. The next morning, they embraced and said their goodbyes. They would see one another again over the next month or so, but they knew this was the real goodbye. Because Sam and Cindy had agreed to host a reunion the following year, though, they could hang on to their friendship that much longer.

Life in Heidelberg went on as normal. There was a feeling of fun in the office with so many people leaving soon. The new recruits were doing well, and Captain Hall was happy that the work of the office would be uninterrupted.

Bob and the others had stopped taking longer auto trips as their time grew shorter. Each looked for a buyer for their car. The pea-green Beetle was in good shape. At that point, Bob only drove it to the Schwimmbad and downtown to hang out at the college or to go to a restaurant in the evening.

It turned out that Ralph liked the car, and he realized that he would need one.

Some of the new recruits had families with money, so buying a car was no problem. One of the new guys bought a beautiful ten-year-old black Porsche 911c. He was going to travel in style. Another was a car nut. He decided to buy a Volkswagen station wagon and replace the engine with a big Porsche engine. That car was a speed demon. And what better place to go those high speeds than on the no-speed-limit Autobahn? On the highway, folks would stare in disbelief as this Volkswagen flew past them, accelerating all the way.

Ralph didn't have lots of money, so the pea-green Beetle appealed to him. He also liked that Bob wasn't jacking up the price, asking only the same $200 he had paid for it 17 months ago. So, they struck a deal. Ralph would forgo getting a car for the next month, and he would get the Beetle in September. Bob agreed not to put the car at risk by driving too much. Deal done!

**August**

By the beginning of August, Bob and his friends were making their preparations to go home. In the second week of August, Bob shipped home his stereo equipment and most of his clothing.

He called Sarah. All was well at home with Henry and Anna, Warner and Yolande. He asked her to be on the lookout for the clothes and stereo. She would be notified when they arrived, and she should ask Warner to help her pick them up. She agreed.

Bob told her a little of his plans. He knew she wouldn't understand how much he had changed and what he wanted when he returned, but he did tell her that he planned to get an apartment and a car. He didn't mention Manhattan.

He told her how valuable the loan from Yolande had been to him. He had a small amount of it left. Although he had agreed to pay it back promptly, he needed to ask if she could extend it and perhaps even add some. He would need that money to get the quick start he wanted. He owed that to himself after serving the country for two years.

Sarah said she understood. "I'll speak to Yolande and ask her about it. I'll let you know. But whatever happens, you can stay with me as long as you want."

"Thanks, Mom," Bob said. "You have been great. I'm counting on you and Yolande more than ever now. When I get back, though, I'll really need my own place."

By mid-August, time was very short for Bob and the others. Bob already had a confirmed flight on Lufthansa from Frankfurt to JFK on September 7. He had few clothes left other than his military ones. Transferring the car to Ralph was easy. They filled out the transfer of ownership form and filed it at the office, along with the bill of sale.

Then Bob was without a car too.

With only a couple of weeks left, the Enlisted Men's club became even more important. No one wanted to drive, travel, or take any undue chances. You didn't want to mess up your trip back to the States. Rich still had his old Ford, though. He wasn't leaving until the beginning of October, so he had a few more weeks to use it.

**The Tunnel**

They took Rich's car downtown on a Friday night later in August. They had dinner in a local restaurant and went to the Tunnel, a jazz club. The Tunnel had been there forever, and many U.S. jazz greats played there as well as at Campbell Barracks. They had just missed Oscar Peterson a couple of weeks before. There was a long line waiting, but they got in at around 11 pm. They went downstairs into what looked like a real tunnel and got a table along the curved wall. It was awesome. In the dark room, illuminated by a blue light, they sat and ordered a bottle of wine. Rich ordered a soda. A very expensive soda. He was driving and didn't want to mess around.

The jazz trio played their first set, and the music was fantastic. Bob and his friends were living within five miles of the venue. It would have been irresponsible not to go. They got back very late. For the second and last time, Bob used Arnie's alarm clock. He still had to do Jeep maintenance on Saturdays. He had never disappointed Sergeant Major Tucker, and he wouldn't begin now.

Saturday was August 24. Bob took care of the Jeep, and Rich later drove some of them to the Schwimmbad.

On Sunday night, they went to the Enlisted Men's club for dinner and the show. They got seated at their usual table in the corner and ordered dinner. Burgers and fries were still the favorites. Some of them ordered the fried flounder left over from Friday.

"Did you see the news about Prague?" Frank asked. "The Russians invaded Czechoslovakia on Wednesday. Two hundred thousand troops and two thousand tanks. That's only six hours from here. You were just on maneuvers with the Seventh Army, Bob. What's going on?"

"I don't know anything," Bob said. "But I know the top brass were concerned. These last Seventh Army tank exercises were being closely watched."

"Come on, Bob, you must know something," Frank said.

"No, I don't," Bob replied. "I wish I could tell you more but I just don't know. I just hope it doesn't lead to war, not only for the Czechs but for us, too. If we get extended here, we might conceivably be assigned to the Seventh Army in combat roles. How crazy would that be with such a short time to go?"

Arnie was always the clear thinker among them. "First, let's all calm down," he said. "This just happened two days ago. Nobody knows anything right now. We should continue with our plans to head home. Only the weeks ahead will tell the story. So, let's not panic until it's time. The odds are with us in this situation."

"You are right, Arnie," Frank said, and they all agreed.

"So, what's going on with you, Frank?" Bob asked.

"I have my flight reservation for September 9. After Fort Dix, I'll fly direct to Los Angeles from Newark. My clothes have already arrived there. I'll take a few days and start work at the dealership. I'm totally pumped."

"Me too," Arnie said. "Although my dad is in Dallas, I'll go straight to Jacksonville and get started. I'll see him for Thanksgiving. What about you Bob?"

"I am very psyched," Bob said. "I've arranged to postpone repaying the loan from my aunt. That cash will help. I'll be looking for a job on Wall Street. But one way or the other, I will quickly move into Manhattan and start my life. I leave here on September 7."

The Zaras were playing at the Enlisted Men's club. They took to the stage and played a great first set. They played amazing covers of the Beatles and other groups, including Spencer Davis, the Rolling Stones, the Righteous Brothers, and many others. Their lead singer, Julie, had an amazing voice. They had all the skills.

"I'm lucky I'll soon be rid of you guys," Rich joked. "You'll all be gone way before I go at the beginning of October. I'll finally get some peace around here."

"Just a minute," Charlie said. "Don't forget the reunion next year. You don't get rid of us that easily."

They laughed.

"Seriously, what will you do when you get home?" Charlie asked.

"Well, that's easy," Rich replied. "I've already accepted a position with the local newspaper back home. With my experience writing for my college newspaper, they were eager to have me. Plus, now that I have two years of experience traveling in Europe and a broader perspective, they agreed to pay me a more-than-average sum of $35,000 per year to start."

"Woooooooooooooooo," the guys whistled.

"Wow! We know who to ask for a loan next year," Arnie said.

"Yeah, right," said Rich. "I'll probably be up to my ears in bills by then."

When the Zaras were midway through their second set, the guys paid the bill and headed back to the barracks.

As August ended, the unsettled times just rolled on. On August 28, the Democratic Party Convention was held in Chicago. Anti-war protests there kicked into a higher gear. The protesters, inspired by Abbie Hoffman, Jerry Rubin, and Tom Hayden, were met by the Chicago Police Department on the streets and in the parks in what would be later described by the investigating governmental commission as a "police riot."

The demonstrators shouted the later famous phrase "The whole world is watching" as they were beaten and arrested by the Chicago police.

In the end, the Democratic Party nominated Hubert Humphrey, defeating Eugene McCarthy and George McGovern.

**September**

The first week of September went by in a flash. On September 6, Bob showed up at the office just to say his goodbyes. He could hardly keep his emotions in check that day. He snuck away very early and hung out at the barracks. He took a long slow jog around the track at the ball field, then just relaxed in the sun until the evening.

On September 7, Rich dropped Bob at Heidelberg train station at 7 am. Bob boarded the train to Frankfurt. From there, a taxi got him to the airport well in time for the 10 am flight to JFK.

Bob sat on the plane in a state of shock. He could hardly process what was happening. He was sad and tremendously excited at the same time.

He was very happy Cindy had agreed to host the reunion the following year. That was like having a life after death. It was something to hang on to. Sarah still hadn't gotten back to him on the loan extension. He would find out about that when he arrived home.

*Boy, a lot is riding on that loan extension. Stay positive,* he thought.

He was lucky enough to get a window seat. Next to him was a businessman, and a younger girl who looked like a college student was on the aisle.

The plane took off on time and slowly climbed to thirty thousand feet. Then it banked to the west for the seven-hour journey to JFK.

Bob had brought a book to read but couldn't concentrate. His mind was racing. Would Yolande come through with the money? How soon could he get his own place? How quickly would he find work?

He had to get a quick start because further back in his mind were all those things that he now knew he had missed growing up. He had a lot of catching up to do.

At the Enlisted Men's club, he had vowed to learn to dance. He had a list a mile long. Learn to dance, see the Statue of Liberty, travel across America (he hadn't even seen the country he'd been protecting for two years), live in Manhattan in his own apartment, and about a thousand other things.

He was incredibly upbeat and shaking with excitement. Life was about to begin!

**The Return**

After a smooth flight, Bob arrived at JFK in the afternoon. He caught a bus to Port Authority Bus Terminal in Manhattan. From there, he got a bus to Fort Dix, New Jersey. He got there late in the afternoon, so there wasn't much to be accomplished that day. He was given a bunk in the barracks near the processing building, had dinner at the mess hall, and turned in early. There were many other soldiers there, waiting to be separated from the service. He did not know any of them, though. He called Sarah and Henry to tell them he'd arrived safely but didn't know how quickly he would get home.

The next morning, things went more quickly than he could have imagined. The machinery that processed soldiers out of active service was well oiled. At 8 am, he went into the processing building, presented his orders to a clerk, and took a seat in the waiting room. One hour later, someone called his name and escorted him into a private office. Not knowing what to expect, Bob was straight-faced despite his excitement. He knew they had to release him. It was just a matter of how long it would take.

To his surprise, his release took place quickly and efficiently. The sergeant carefully reviewed Bob's personnel file, especially the dates, his pay, and the orders releasing him from active duty. By 10:30 am, Bob was no longer on active duty in the U.S. Army. Turns out that when you were drafted into the U.S. Army, your term of service was six years, not two. However, after two years, you were released from active duty and placed on inactive status in the U.S. Army Reserves. That was what had just happened to Bob.

"In all likelihood, this will be your last service," the sergeant told him. "It would require a very unusual circumstance for the army to recall you to active duty. It ain't gonna happen."

"OK. Thanks, Sergeant," Bob said.

They got up and shook hands. Bob was a civilian now.

"Thanks for your service," the sergeant said.

Bob grinned, pumped the handshake, and then turned and left.

As he walked out of the building and toward the bus stop, Bob breathed a sigh of relief, still grinning from ear to ear.

The trip to the Bronx was long. A bus to Trenton, the NJ Transit train to Penn Station in Manhattan, a shuttle to the east side, then the number 4 IRT train to 167th Street and Jerome Avenue in the Bronx. It was a long and complicated trip, but it gave Bob time to think. His mind was spinning with all the possibilities and his desire to get a fast start on his future.

He stared at the green duffel bag on the seat next to him. It was like a person who had been his companion for two years.

Bob walked the few blocks to Sarah's on Walton Avenue in the dimming light of late afternoon. He'd had no time to call, so he just showed up. Sarah's eyes lit up.

They hugged for a long time. Sarah was crying. "Why didn't you call?" she asked. "Never mind, I am so happy to see you."

Bob was emotional too. "Love you too, Mom. I'm very glad to be home."

They ate dinner together, then Bob turned in for the night.

Bob got an early start the next morning. He wanted to see the old neighborhood and some of his old haunts. Like a last touch of the base before starting his new life.

He walked around the neighborhood for an hour. Taft High School, the Grand Concourse, $167^{th}$ street, where the $167^{th}$ Street Cafeteria and the pool room were. Then $170^{th}$ Street and Warner's Fish Market.

To Bob, the Bronx looked strange. The buildings on the streets looked decrepit, dingy, and crowded. At his mom's building, the shrubs in the main courtyard were gone and paved over. Pavement was everywhere. The life-affirming greenery that he had come to love in Heidelberg was nowhere. He had gone from a small rural college town to a densely packed urban neighborhood enveloped in concrete.

The Bronx had changed. It was darker than he remembered. It was far bleaker than he remembered. It had nothing to offer him, and just being there felt strange after life in Heidelberg. He was shocked and angry. He redoubled his vow to get out quickly. In truth, it was Bob who had changed. Over the past two years, he had seen a glimpse of the life he wanted, of a life worth fighting for, and he meant to fight for it. He was "all in."

The next day, Bob took a trip further afield. He visited the Statue of Liberty as he had promised he would. He took the train to lower Manhattan and then the ferry to Liberty Island. Reading the inscriptions was emotional. He contemplated their meaning and his service in the U.S. Army over the past two years.

On the way back, he walked a long way from the Battery to Greenwich Village. There, he saw a low-rise village, bathed in greenery. There were lots of shops and jazz clubs. There was electricity in the air. It reminded him of Heidelberg. He wondered if his future would take him there.

Later, back in the Bronx, he waited for Sarah to return from work at Ohrbach's. Over dinner, he asked her about money.

"Mom, have you spoken to Yolande about the loan extension?" he asked. "I just can't stay here in the Bronx any longer. Other than you, mom, there is nothing here for me." Sarah looked sad but said nothing. "You know, I'm not going far, that's for sure. I will visit you often, but I just can't stay here."

At that, Sarah brightened a little. "It's good news. Yolande agreed to wait for repayment and to lend you another $3,000. She and Warner are glad you are back. She added one requirement, though. She said you would have to keep working at the fish market."

Bob grinned. It was unlike Sarah to joke like that. They smiled and hugged.

Bob was elated. The additional money was the most important first step. Now he could look for an inexpensive apartment in Manhattan at the same time as looking for work.

The next day, he got a phone call from Rich, the friend who had helped him learn to drive in his BMW. "I heard you are back and figured it would be good to connect.

Some of us will be in the 167th Street pool room around 4 if you can make it."

Bob said he would and hung up. At around 4 that afternoon, he walked the two blocks to the pool room. He went inside and walked down the same decrepit old staircase into a pool room of about twenty-five tables. The room was far dingier than he remembered. Memories of far too much time spent there flooded back. He shook hands with a few of the guys he knew.

He told them a few stories about the army and Germany, but he didn't discuss any of his plans. He noticed they didn't seem to be any different from two years ago. They asked him to play a game of pool. Bob declined, saying he just wanted to watch. He had just shown up to say hello.

They told Bob they were going to Yonkers Raceway that evening and asked if he wanted to come along. Rich would drive.

Bob said he would think about it. But after five minutes, he realized that nothing had changed there. Not his friends, not the conversations, not the time-wasting things they did. His stomach started to hurt. He started breathing faster. He was panicking. He saw his life flashing in front of him. All those wonderful experiences in Europe, all the friendships, the dinners, the music, and the thousands of promises he had made to himself about making his life better flashed in front of his eyes. He instantly knew that none of his old friends could see him as the person he had become.

He grabbed his stomach and said, "Guys, I'm not feeling well. Must be something I ate. I had lunch at the 170th Street Diner. I have to go, sorry."

He ran out of there as fast as he could and kept going the two blocks to his house. That was the clincher. He did not respond to their telephone calls the next day, or the day after that.

He knew for sure that he was alone and he had to act quickly. He had to cut out this part of his life. He had to quickly move on to his new life or be dragged down by the quicksand that was life in the Bronx. Sarah, too, did not really understand him or see him in the light of the Bob he planned to be.

Two years of wandering – from the Bronx to South Carolina to Georgia and then to Heidelberg – had awakened the desire to live a fuller, more interesting life. He was smart enough to envision it and willing enough to make sacrifices to make it happen. It simply could not be done in the Bronx.

So began a sixty-day blur of activity. Home only a week, he started to hang out in Manhattan. He had a model of the life he wanted, and he searched for it in Manhattan. He found an example of it at a place called the Village Gate in Greenwich Village. Greenwich Village was a small town within a big town. The buildings were low rise, and there was plenty of grass on the sidewalks and a couple of nice parks. It was a college town, too. The sprawling NYU campus had Washington Square Park as its centerpiece, and Bob began to spend a little time there some days.

One evening, he wandered past the Village Gate and went inside. A jazz trio was playing. Bob ordered a Johnnie Walker Black on the rocks and sat back to enjoy the music. The room was busy. It had a nice warm, yellowish glow created by the lighting.

The jazz trio was led by Junior Mance, a popular pianist who played there often. The music was incredible. Bob closed his eyes and was back in Heidelberg. He stayed for both sets, then took the cumbersome train trip back to the Bronx. He had found what he was looking for.

The music at the Village Gate was a direct connection between the life he'd had in Heidelberg and the life he envisioned in Manhattan. Whenever Junior Mance was on the bill, Bob was there.

Junior Mance was about forty years old. From Illinois originally, he had been playing piano since he was five. He had a long, rich musical history. That September, Mance recorded an album called "Live at the Top" for Atlantic Records. Bob lamented not being at the Village Gate when it was recorded.

There were difficulties ahead. Bob was turned down many times for Wall Street jobs, the money started to dwindle, and each return to the Bronx felt like a setback. But the music sustained him. It was his guardian angel. It was as if the music had become a message:

*Remember who you are and the life you want.*

*Don't worry. You might have failed this time,*

*but you will succeed eventually.*

*Never give up because I'm here with you.*

Finally, after two months, Bob was offered a job doing administrative work at a large brokerage firm in lower Manhattan. He accepted right away. The pay was low, but the future was bright.

Bob was overjoyed. He went home to the Bronx in an exultant mood. Over dinner with Sarah, he told her he now had a job and would redouble his efforts to find an apartment in Manhattan. She had made her special pot roast to celebrate. She knew Bob loved that. She had also begun to realize how much he had changed, that he was serious, and that he would not be with her much longer.

In the middle of dinner, Sarah said, "You know, my dear, I have to confess something to you."

"What's that?" Bob asked.

"Well, I didn't know if I would ever tell you this, and I swore Yolande to secrecy. But I see how much you have changed since you've been away. You are not the same boy you were. I can see that you are a man now, and have matured."

"Uh-oh!" Bob said. "Sounds serious."

"When we gave you the loan last year, Yolande couldn't really spare the money. So, it was really me that advanced you the money. I couldn't tell you then. I was afraid if you knew the loan came from me, you might not pay it back so fast, and I might have needed it to move into Co-Op City. Yolande agreed to keep it secret. I want you to know how sorry I am that I didn't trust you then. It's plain now how you have changed, and I'm not worried at all."

Bob got up from the table. Both had tears in their eyes as they hugged.

"I totally forgive you, Mom," Bob said. "I would be nothing without you. You have been the greatest mom. Thank you so much for telling me this now. It shows me you think I've changed for the better."

They sat back down and finished dinner in a cheerful mood. Sarah had also made her special chocolate pudding for dessert.

Bob would start his job in one week. That made it urgent for him to spend the next week looking for an apartment in Manhattan, but his brother Henry was living with Anna in Kew Gardens, Queens, and he wanted to visit them. Anna and Henry had reconciled and quickly married. Bob had been in Heidelberg, so he had missed the wedding, but he and Sarah were thrilled for them.

The next day, Bob took the train to Kew Gardens. Anna made a great lunch, and they went out to Forest Park, a large park nearby. Bob noticed they had bicycles. He asked

Henry to take one along and confessed that he had never ridden a bike and asked Henry to show him how. Bob was very conscious of the huge list of things he had never done and took advantage of the moment. At the park, there was a long, gradually sloped paved trail.

"Bob, this trail is ideal," Henry said. "What you are going to do is just sit on the bike and let it roll downhill. No pedaling. This will teach you balance. Once you have done that a few times, you'll see how easy it is. Then you can do it again while pedaling too."

After just a few trips gliding down the long trail, Bob got the hang of it, and then pedaled back up the hill. Another item on Bob's huge list checked off. Bob made a mental note to buy a bike once he got set up in Manhattan.

They hugged goodbye. Bob congratulated them on their marriage again, then left to get the train back to the Bronx.

The next morning, he went to Greenwich Village to look for an apartment. He walked everywhere, stopping at places with *For Rent* signs, even talking to people he encountered on the street.

"Do you know of any apartments available?" No one could help. There were some available apartments, but all were way too expensive for Bob.

On Grove Street, he saw an older man sweeping the street in front of a gated group of three-story brownstones called Grove Court. Bob struck up a conversation, and the fellow was friendly. Turned out he owned one of the three brownstones and lived there. Amazingly, the entire building was one apartment with three rooms, one on each floor. They call those "Trinity" houses. The owner finished sweeping and invited Bob in for a coffee. He showed Bob the whole house. It really was just three small rooms, one on each floor. He had inherited the house from his parents. They spoke for about an hour. He told Bob there was nothing inexpensive available in the neighborhood, but he gave him a few leads. They didn't work out, but Bob didn't despair. *Someday, I'll live around here,* he thought.

Realizing the challenge in Greenwich Village was the small number of apartments, he started looking on the Upper West Side of Manhattan the next day. He walked around some neighborhoods and finally saw a storefront with some signs for *Apartment Rentals*. He walked in and chatted with a broker. She was a pretty blonde who had been working there for a couple of years. She showed Bob about six places that morning. Finally, he saw a small studio apartment in a nice building just off Central Park West. It was the size of a postage stamp, but Bob took it. They went back to the storefront, and he signed the lease. Done! He would be living in Manhattan in two weeks, in a tiny apartment costing $206 per month.

During the conversation, she asked Bob what he did for a living. Bob was taken aback. "Well, I guess I'm in the financial business." She looked at him quizzically. "Last week, I was in the U.S. Army, serving in Europe. Today I am here, and in the financial business."

He told her about the job at the downtown brokerage company. She smiled and said, "Congratulations, Bob. Maybe we'll go out to lunch next week to celebrate."

She gave him another big smile. Bob smiled back and said, "Sure, I'd like that. I'll call you next week."

Bob decided to go to the Village Gate that night to celebrate. It turned out that Junior Mance was performing.

Arriving during the first set, Bob took the only open seat left at the bar. A good omen. The bartender waved to Bob and brought him a Johnnie Walker Black on the rocks. Bob relaxed in his seat and listened. He closed his eyes and smiled.

Although there were no lyrics, the music seemed to be saying *Congratulations. I told you, you would succeed. I said you would travel on the road to the life you want.*

The first set ended. The bartender brought a drink over to Junior Mance. Mance sipped it and relaxed in his seat at the piano. Bob took advantage of the moment. He walked up to the piano and introduced himself to Mance. He mentioned Heidelberg and the jazz clubs there.

"I love your music. You are the man," Bob said.

Junior Mance smiled, and they shook hands. Then Bob walked back to his seat at the bar. He sipped his drink, thought about the future, and waited to enjoy the second set.

## Acknowledgements

My friends George Tepper and Shyamal Sen encouraged me throughout the process of writing this book. They read the manuscript, chapter by chapter, and provided me with valuable feedback all along the way. Special thanks go to Shyamal Sen for his valuable advice, not only about how to improve the book but also about how to improve the writing. On this journey, in many ways, I learned to write from him.

My wife Allison encouraged me continuously. She read the manuscript many times and provided very valuable advice on improving it.

My editor Marc Murphy-Robinson played an important role in improving the quality of the book. He kept me out of trouble by highlighting various issues, and his editing skill greatly improved the book's readability.

My cover designer Ken Leeder took the time to understand the meaning of the story and the nature of the main character in order to create the book's beautiful cover.


To contact me, please visit my website: www.barrysinger.co

Made in the USA
Middletown, DE
25 June 2022

67359640R00159